INFORMATION
THEORY
AND
CODING

NORMAN ABRAMSON

Associate Professor of Electrical Engineering
Stanford University

INFORMATION
THEORY
AND
CODING

New York
San Francisco
Toronto
London

McGRAW-HILL *Book Company*

Information Theory and Coding

III

PREFACE

This book has evolved from a set of notes on information theory and binary coding prepared for a sequence of lectures at ITT Federal Laboratories. Subsequently, these notes were enlarged and used as the text for a one-quarter graduate course in electrical engineering at Stanford University. Most of the final version of the manuscript was developed during a one-semester course in information theory at the IBM Research Laboratories, San Jose, California.

The purpose of this book is to present the basic ideas of information theory unencumbered, in so far as possible, by the mathematics used to express these ideas.   It is possible to treat information theory purely as a mathematical study of the properties of certain abstract quantities over which some probability measure is defined.   Our interest, however, will be in the relevance of the theory to the real world and in correspondences between the quantities we study and certain natural concepts of importance in a wide number of fields.   In order to fully develop the significance of these correspondences we use mathematics as a language in which to express information theory.   The important theorems of information theory are stated and proved rigorously.   Complete proofs are provided for all assertions, and no appeal to intuition is used except in *interpreting* the results derived.

In spite of this the mathematical prerequisites are quite modest. A knowledge of logarithms and an intuitive understanding of the meaning of probabilities and of average values are all that is necessary.   Calculus is *not* used in this book.   At the same time the nonmathematical reader should be warned that without some familiarity with simple mathematical arguments a good deal of time will be required to understand certain steps in the proofs presented.   The proofs themselves, however, and their significance will not require a mathematics background.

This simplicity has been achieved by limiting the mathematical generality of our treatment.   Only information sources with a finite number of output symbols and a finite memory are treated. The only information channels discussed have a finite number of input and output symbols and zero memory.   These restrictions allow us to develop all the important concepts of the theory of information.   The price we pay for these restrictions is mathematical elegance.   For those interested in such elegance, however, it is a simple matter to generalize by planting the proofs given here in a Borel field.

The material in this book has been tested in both university and industrial classes.   It can be comfortably covered in one semester by students in electrical engineering, operations research, or computer science.   Students with more extensive mathematical background or specialized interests may wish to investigate in more detail certain advanced topics treated in the notes at the end of each chapter.   These notes are meant to suggest a number of interesting research areas in information theory.   Problems are also included at the end of each chapter; those problems preceded by a star require the use of calculus for solution.

I am indebted to a number of people for their help in the preparation of this book.   Dr. Richard Hamming provided a particularly detailed review of an early version.   Other helpful comments were provided by Professors David Braverman, Thomas Kailath, and Wesley Peterson.   The manuscript has benefited from corrections and clarifications suggested by students at Stanford.   A number of suggestions by Thomas Cover, Arthur Geoffrion, and David Howell are incorporated in this text.   A large number of errors and misprints were weeded out of the notes by two classes at Stanford and one at IBM Research Laboratories to whom I now make a confession: I did not really base your grades on the lists of corrections you provided.

Norman Abramson

CONTENTS

GLOSSARY OF SYMBOLS AND ENTROPY EXPRESSIONS

$$
\boxed{\begin{array}{c}\text{Information}\\\text{source}\end{array}} \rightarrow
\left.\begin{array}{c} s_1 \\ s_2 \\ \cdot \\ \cdot \\ \cdot \\ s_q \end{array}\right\} S \quad
\left.\begin{array}{c} x_1 \\ x_2 \\ \cdot \\ \cdot \\ \cdot \\ x_r \end{array}\right\} X \quad
s_i \rightarrow X_i = (x_{i_1}, x_{i_2}, \ldots, x_{i_j})
$$

$$
\begin{array}{cc} \text{Source} & \text{Code} \\ \text{alphabet} & \text{alphabet} \end{array} \qquad\qquad \text{Code word}
$$

FIGURE G-1. Coding an information source.

$$A \begin{cases} a_1 \\ a_2 \\ \cdot \\ \cdot \\ \cdot \\ a_r \end{cases} \to \boxed{\begin{array}{c} \text{Information} \\ \text{channel} \end{array}} \to \begin{cases} b_1 \\ b_2 \\ \cdot \\ \cdot \\ \cdot \\ b_s \end{cases} B$$

Input alphabet   Output alphabet

FIGURE G-2. An information channel.

G-2. General Symbols

S	source alphabet
s_i	source symbol
q	number of source symbols
S^n	nth extension of source alphabet
σ_i	symbol from nth extension of source alphabet
$\bar{S}$	adjoint of source S
P_i	probability of source symbol s_i

X	code alphabet
x_i	code symbol
r	number of code symbols (also, number of channel input symbols)
X_i	code word (a sequence of x_i's) corresponding to s_i
l_i	number of code symbols in code word X_i corresponding to s_i
λ_i	number of code symbols in code word corresponding to σ_i
L	average length of a code word for S
L_n	average length of a code word for S^n

A	channel input alphabet
a_i	channel input symbol
r	number of channel input symbols (also, number of code symbols)
A^n	nth extension of channel input alphabet
α_i	symbol from nth extension of channel input alphabet

B	channel output alphabet
b_j	channel output symbol
s	number of channel output symbols
B^n	nth extension of channel output alphabet
β_j	symbol from nth extension of channel output alphabet

m	order of a Markov source
P_{ij}	element of a channel matrix; the probability of receiving b_j if a_i is sent
p	error probability of a BSC ($\bar{p} = 1 - p$)
C	channel capacity
P_E	error probability
M	number of messages in a code

R information rate
D hamming distance
$d(b_j)$ decision rule

G-3. Entropy Expressions

$$I(s_i) = \log \frac{1}{P(s_i)}$$

the amount of information obtained when s_i is received (zero-memory source)

$$I(s_i/s_j) = \log \frac{1}{P(s_i/s_j)}$$

the amount of information obtained when s_i is received after s_j has been received (first-order Markov source)

$$H(S) = \sum_S P(s_i) \log \frac{1}{P(s_i)}$$

entropy of the zero-memory source S

$$H(S/s_j) = \sum_{i=1}^{q} P(s_i/s_j) \log \frac{1}{P(s_i/s_j)}$$

conditional entropy of the first-order Markov source S

$$H(S) = \sum_{S^2} P(s_i,\, s_j) \log \frac{1}{P(s_i/s_j)}$$

entropy of the first-order Markov source S

$$H_r(S) = \frac{H(S)}{\log r}$$

entropy, measured in r-ary units

$$H(\omega) = \omega \log \frac{1}{\omega} + (1 - \omega) \log \frac{1}{1 - \omega}$$

entropy function (Figure 2-3)

$$H(A) = \sum_A P(a) \log \frac{1}{P(a)}$$

entropy of input alphabet A (a priori entropy)

$$H(A/b_j) = \sum_A P(a/b_j) \log \frac{1}{P(a/b_j)}$$

conditional entropy of A (a posteriori entropy)

$$H(A/B) = \sum_{A,B} P(a,\, b) \log \frac{1}{P(a/b)}$$

equivocation of A with respect to B

$$H(A,\, B) = \sum_{A,B} P(a,\, b) \log \frac{1}{P(a,\, b)}$$

joint entropy of A and B

$$I(A;\, B) = H(A) - H(A/B)$$

mutual information of A and B

$$I(a;\, B) = \sum_B P(b/a) \log \frac{P(b/a)}{P(b)}$$

conditional mutual information

$$H(A, B/C) = \sum_{A,B,C} P(a, b, c) \log \frac{1}{P(a, b/c)}$$

equivocation of A and B with respect to C

$$H(A/B, C) = \sum_{A,B,C} P(a, b, c) \log \frac{1}{P(a/b, c)}$$

equivocation of A with respect to B and C

$I(A; B/C) = H(A/C) - H(A/B, C)$ mutual information of A and B, given C

$I(A; B; C) = I(A; B) - I(A; B/C)$ mutual information of A, B, and C

1

INTRODUCTION

1-1. What Information Theory Is Not

Information theory is a remarkably appealing name to assign to a scientific discipline; when applied to the subject matter of this book, it is also somewhat deceptive. The origins of information theory date back to Claude E. Shannon's publication of a paper in the *Bell System Technical Journal* in 1948 (Shannon, 1948).† Shannon, perhaps realizing the deceptive qualities of the word

† References indicated in parentheses may be found in the list of References at the end of the book.

1

information, called his paper A Mathematical Theory of Communication. In terms of the colloquial meaning of information, Shannon's paper deals with the carriers of information—symbols—and not with information itself. It deals with communication and the means of communication rather than that elusive end product of communication—information.

The distinction we wish to make here is an important one. Starting in Chapter 2, we shall derive a number of fundamental properties of symbols used to transmit information. We shall learn that the symbols must obey certain laws if they are to be capable of transmitting information; we shall relate properties of the symbols to the amount of information they can convey. Whether a given symbol under consideration actually does convey information, however, will in general depend upon factors outside the scope of our theory. For example, "le soleil brille" will convey information to only some of the readers of this book. A common language facilitates the transmission of information. Slightly less obvious are psychological factors which can affect information. The sentence "The sun is shining" may conceivably have more than meteorological implications if heard by a psychotic. Semantic factors can cause the same set of words to convey various meanings to various listeners. Shannon (1948) has commented that "the semantic aspects of communication are irrelevant to the engineering problem." Weaver (1949) has pointed out, however, that the reverse is not necessarily true—that the engineering (or technical) aspects of communication may be relevant to the semantic, psychological, and linguistic aspects. In Section 2-8 we illustrate the application of the theory developed in this book to linguistics. Except for Section 2-8 and certain notes at the end of each chapter, we do not treat the more specialized applications of information theory to other fields.

We shall treat the central ideas of the theory of information, with particular stress on information measure and its interpretation. The reader may wish to investigate in greater detail the application of information theory to some other field. The possibilities here are almost endless. The material discussed in this book can be related to the information provided by a statistical experiment (Lindley, 1956; Kullback, 1959; Grettenberg, 1962). We shall see that the concept of entropy, central to information theory as treated here, has at least a formal equivalence with the entropy of thermodynamics (Brillouin, 1956; Jaynes, 1959). The applications of information theory to psychology (Quastler, 1956), art (Pierce, 1961, pp. 250–267), and semantics (Bar-Hillel and Carnap, 1952) have been explored. Finally, the reader is referred to a stimulating treatment of some theological aspects of information theory (Elias, 1958).

1-2. What Information Theory Is

The first step in our study of information will be to define a measure of information and to investigate the properties of this measure. The properties we investigate will lend an air of plausibility to our measure, and will aid in relating the mathematical theory to the physical model motivating the theory. It is important to note, however, that the justification for our definition of an information measure cannot be obtained by relationships contained entirely within the framework of the definition. It is clear that we may set up a framework of information theory which, taken by itself, is self-consistent and quite reasonable. Yet such a framework without further justification would constitute merely a mathematical discipline. It is only in the relationship of the framework which we erect to quantities entirely apart from this framework that the justification for the theory can be found. Thus we shall derive a definition of information and a set of relationships for our definition which taken by themselves are quite reasonable. The definition of information, however, will not be justified by the internal consistency of the relationships, but by showing how these relationships apply to quantities not involved in the information theory framework. In order to emphasize this necessity for correspondence between our mathematical model and the physical world, we shall use this introductory chapter to ask several important questions which may be formulated in a manner completely independent of any particular information measure. In Chapters 2, 3, and 4 we shall see how our definition of information provides quantitative and mathematically sound answers to these questions.

1-3. Encoding Information

Let us consider some examples of information transmission in order to introduce the basic ideas of information theory. We restrict ourselves at first to consideration of a particularly simple but important type of information—binary information. Examples of binary information are easy to cite. The information stored in punched cards, messages transmitted by on-or-off teletype systems, and the information stored in bistable elements of electronic computers are but a few such examples. Restricting the remainder of this chapter to information of this form will greatly simplify the points we wish to make.

It is interesting to note that, contrary to popular belief, the binary representation of information is not relatively new, but has been known for quite a while. In fact, an early reference to the importance of binary information is given in Matthew 5:37: "But let your communication be Yea, yea; Nay, nay: for whatsoever is more than these cometh of evil." This point of view may be somewhat extreme, and we shall consider the theory of information in terms of both binary and nonbinary information, starting in Chapter 2.

A simple example of the representation of nonbinary information in terms of the binary digits 0 and 1 is given in Table 1-1.

TABLE 1-1. BINARY CODING OF THE DECIMAL DIGITS

Decimal digit	Binary representation
0	0000
1	0001
2	0010
3	0011
4	0100
5	0101
6	0110
7	0111
8	1000
9	1001

The correspondence of binary sequences to decimal digits given in Table 1-1 is a simple example of a *code*. The 10 binary sequences of Table 1-1 are called *code words*, and the 10 decimal digits are called the *message symbols*. In Section 3-1 we shall define a code and code words more carefully.   For the present, however, we can be somewhat imprecise in our discussion.   Clearly we may obtain a sequence of binary digits for any sequence of decimal digits (message symbols) by the use of the code of Table 1-1.   Conversely, from a sequence of binary digits arising from this code, we may work backward to obtain a unique sequence of decimal digits.

The possibility of working backward from a string of binary code words to the corresponding message symbols is not always straightforward.   For example, consider the code defined by Table 1-2.

TABLE 1-2. A BINARY CODE

Message symbols	Code words
s_1	0
s_2	01
s_3	001
s_4	111

If we are given a sequence of code words from this code, we may not be able to work backward to a unique set of message symbols. The binary sequence

$$111001 \qquad\qquad (1\text{-}1)$$

might have arisen from

$$s_4 s_3 \qquad\qquad (1\text{-}2)$$

or from

$$s_4 s_1 s_2 \qquad\qquad (1\text{-}3)$$

Now the reader may object here and point out that the insertion of a comma (or space) is all that is needed.   This is, of course, true; the use of a comma (or space), however, contradicts our assumption of a binary code.   If we use a comma to separate code words, we are in effect using three symbols for the code—zero, one, and comma.

It is easy to find a code which does not suffer from the difficulties of the code of Table 1-2.   If we are given a sequence of code words of the code of Table 1-3, we may work backward to determine a

unique set of message symbols.   In this chapter we concern ourselves only with such codes.

TABLE 1-3. A BINARY CODE

Message symbols	Code words
s_1	0
s_2	10
s_3	110
s_4	1110

1-4. A Problem in Information Transmission

To illustrate some of the ideas of coding and their relationship
to the measurement of information, let us consider the following
problem.   It is desired to set up a communication system between
San Francisco and New York.   The system is to transmit the
state of the weather in San Francisco at given time intervals.   The
system is required to use only on-off (i.e., binary) equipment.   To
simplify matters, it is desired to classify the state of weather in
San Francisco in one of four possible conditions—sunny, cloudy,
rainy, or foggy.   These four possible conditions may be considered
to comprise the four message symbols as shown in Table 1-4.   Also
shown in Table 1-4 are the probabilities assumed for each of the
states.   We assume that the four states are equiprobable.

TABLE 1-4. THE STATE OF THE WEATHER IN SAN FRANCISCO

Messages	Probabilities
Sunny	$\frac{1}{4}$
Cloudy	$\frac{1}{4}$
Rainy	$\frac{1}{4}$
Foggy	$\frac{1}{4}$

One possible method of encoding these messages into a sequence
of binary symbols is to set up the following correspondence, called
code a.

Code α

Sunny	00
Cloudy	01
Rainy	10
Foggy	11

(1-4)

Thus, using code α, "sunny, foggy, foggy, cloudy" would be coded as "00111101."

It is clear that code α is an acceptable code for the transmission of this information in the sense that, given a sequence of code words, we may work backward to reconstruct a unique sequence of messages which gave rise to that particular sequence of code words.

It is also clear that using code α, it is necessary to send 2 binary digits (binits)† for each message. Furthermore, the reader may easily satisfy himself that it is not possible to find another acceptable code which allows one to use *less* than 2 binits per message.

Now consider a similar problem presented to an engineer in Los Angeles. That is, it is desired to set up a similar binary communication system to transmit the state of the weather in Los Angeles to New York. We know that there are important meteorological differences between San Francisco and Los Angeles weather. One of these is accounted for by classifying the state of the Los Angeles weather as sunny, cloudy, rainy, or *smoggy*. Now, although the difference between fog and smog is not inconsiderable to a resident of one of these cities, it does not appear to be a factor in the design of the communications system. Since the four states are coded into binary sequences, the significance or meaning of a particular sequence is irrelevant from a communications point of view.

Another meteorological difference can exist, however, which is definitely not irrelevant to the communications problem. In all fairness to the climate of Los Angeles, we must assign different probabilities to the four possible states. These are shown in Table 1-5.

† From this point on we shall make use of the contraction *binit* for binary digit. It is important to make a distinction between the binit (binary digit) and the *bit* (a unit of information which we shall define in Chapter 2). As we shall see, a binit may contain one bit of information under certain circumstances.

TABLE 1-5. THE STATE OF THE WEATHER IN LOS ANGELES

Messages	Probabilities
Sunny	$\frac{1}{4}$
Cloudy	$\frac{1}{8}$
Rainy	$\frac{1}{8}$
Smoggy	$\frac{1}{2}$

If we use code $\mathcal{C}$ to transmit this information, we shall do as well as, but not better than, the communication system transmitting from San Francisco. That is, if we use code $\mathcal{C}$, we send 2 binits per message regardless of the state of the weather. Consider, however, the possibility of using the following code, called code $\mathcal{B}$, to transmit the information:

$$\begin{array}{ll} & \text{Code } \mathcal{B} \\ \text{Sunny} & 10 \\ \text{Cloudy} & 110 \\ \text{Rainy} & 1110 \\ \text{Smoggy} & 0 \end{array} \qquad (1\text{-}5)$$

Using code $\mathcal{B}$ to transmit the message "sunny, smoggy, smoggy, cloudy," we would send "1000110."

Again, any binary sequence coming from this code gives rise to a unique sequence of messages. This is true since every binary sequence corresponding to a message ends in a 0 and thus the 0 may be thought of as signaling the end of a code word. The average length L (in binits) of a code word using code $\mathcal{B}$ may be calculated as

$$\begin{aligned} L &= 2\,\Pr\,(\text{sunny}) + 3\,\Pr\,(\text{cloudy}) + 4\,\Pr\,(\text{rainy}) + 1\,\Pr\,(\text{smoggy}) \\ &= 2(\tfrac{1}{4}) + 3(\tfrac{1}{8}) + 4(\tfrac{1}{8}) + 1(\tfrac{1}{2}) \\ &= 1\tfrac{7}{8} \text{ binits/message} \end{aligned} \qquad (1\text{-}6)$$

That is, for our communication system from Los Angeles to New York we have found a method of transmitting information about the state of the weather, using an average of only $1\tfrac{7}{8}$ binits per message, rather than 2 binits per message. The reader may verify that if code $\mathcal{B}$ is used for transmitting the weather in San Francisco (Table 1-4), a value of $L = 2\tfrac{1}{2}$ binits per message will result. We have thus shown that it is possible to transmit the same type of

reason for 1⅓ binits/message is that
the shortest code word you used for the message
with the longest probab.

information from Los Angeles using about 6 per cent fewer binits per message, on the average. A reduction of 6 per cent in the number of binary digits to be transmitted in a practical communication system is a gain of some importance. Furthermore, this gain has been achieved by the simple expedient of using different labels for the messages sent.

1-5. Some Questions

The example given in the previous section raises several questions of a fundamental nature. First of all, achieving a gain of 6 per cent in so simple a fashion has whetted our appetite for further improvement. Can we, then, obtain additional improvement of this sort by relabeling the messages in an even cleverer fashion? If further improvement is possible (and in this particular example it is), how far can we go? That is, what is the minimum number of binits per message which we are required to use in order to transmit this information? Once we have established the minimum value of L, the problem of actually constructing a code which achieves this minimum value arises. What are some practical methods of synthesizing such codes?

The last of the questions suggested by our simple example is "Why?" What differences are there in the situations described for Los Angeles and San Francisco which allow us to use fewer binits in order to transmit the state of the weather for Los Angeles? This last question is certainly the most fundamental. In other terms, the question may be restated as "What is the nature of information?" The fact that we need fewer binits for the weather in Los Angeles implies that, in some sense, providing the state of the weather in Los Angeles gives less information than providing the state of the weather in San Francisco. We shall see that this vague notion of *amount of information* may be made precise by the proper definition of a measure of information. From the example given in Section 1-4, it is clear that the definition of information is concerned with the probability of occurrence of the various messages.

In the next three chapters we shall find answers to these questions by defining an information measure based on the message probabilities. That is, we shall obtain the minimum value for the average number of binits per message which we must use; we shall derive methods of constructing codes which will allow us to achieve this minimum, and, finally, we shall discuss the nature of information itself.

NOTES

Note 1.   An easily read mathematician's view of information theory can be found in an expository article by McMillan (1953).   McMillan also presents an amusing description of a mathematician's view of a communication engineer's view of information theory.

Note 2.   Some appreciation of the tremendous range of information theory (in the wide sense) may be obtained from an examination of approximately four thousand entries in Stumpers's bibliographies of information theory (1953, 1955, 1957, 1960).

PROBLEM

1-1.   In Section 1-4 we found two codes, code α and code $\mathcal{B}$, useful in transmitting the state of the weather in Los Angeles.   The average length of code α was 2 binits per message, and the average length of code $\mathcal{B}$ was $1\frac{7}{8}$ binits per message.   In Chapter 4 we shall show that the smallest possible average length of a code for the problem of Table 1-5 is $1\frac{3}{4}$ binits per message.   Furthermore, we shall find a method of generating such a code.

Without looking ahead into Chapter 4, try your hand at finding a code which achieves this minimum average length.   Remember that sequences of words of your code must represent a unique sequence of messages.

2

INFORMATION
AND SOURCES

2-1. The Definition of Information

In Chapter 1, we formulated several fundamental questions about the nature of information. In order to answer these questions, we now define a measure of information, and show that this measure has certain properties which we should demand of any reasonable information measure. Note, however, the fact that we are able to show the reasonableness and the internal consistency of our definition does not provide a justification for the definition. We shall justify the definition only by answering the questions posed

11

in Chapter 1—questions which did not depend upon any particular definition of information—in terms of our definition.

> *Definition.*   Let E be some event which occurs with probability $P(E)$.   If we are told that event E has occurred, then we say we have received

$$I(E) = \log \frac{1}{P(E)} \qquad (2\text{-}1)$$

> units of information.

The choice of base for the logarithm in the above definition amounts to a choice of the unit we use for information, since

$$\log_a x = \frac{1}{\log_b a} \log_b x \qquad (2\text{-}2)$$

If we use a logarithm to the base 2, the resulting unit of information is called the *bit* (a contraction of *binary unit*).

$$I(E) = \log_2 \frac{1}{P(E)} \qquad \text{bits} \qquad (2\text{-}3a)$$

If we use the natural logarithm, the resulting unit of information is called the *nat* (a contraction of *natural unit*).

$$I(E) = \ln \frac{1}{P(E)} \qquad \text{nats} \qquad (2\text{-}3b)$$

If we use a logarithm to the base 10, then the unit of information is the *Hartley*.   It was R. V. Hartley who first suggested the use of a logarithmic measure of information (Hartley, 1928).

$$I(E) = \log_{10} \frac{1}{P(E)} \qquad \text{Hartleys} \qquad (2\text{-}3c)$$

In general, if we use a logarithm to the base r,

$$I(E) = \log_r \frac{1}{P(E)} \qquad r\text{-ary units} \qquad (2\text{-}3d)$$

From (2-2), we see that

$$1 \text{ Hartley} = 3.32 \text{ bits} \qquad (2\text{-}4a)$$
$$1 \text{ nat} = 1.44 \text{ bits} \qquad (2\text{-}4b)$$

We note, also, that if $P(E) = \frac{1}{2}$, then $I(E) = 1$ bit.   That is, *one bit is the amount of information we obtain when one of two possible equally likely alternatives is specified.*   Such a situation may occur when one flips a coin or examines the output of a binary communication system.

To obtain a feel for the amount of information transmitted in a modern communication system, consider a single television picture. Such a picture may be thought of as an array of black, white, and gray dots, with roughly 500 rows and 600 columns.   We shall assume that each of these $500 \times 600 = 300{,}000$ dots may take on any one of 10 distinguishable brightness levels, so that there are $10^{300,000}$ different possible TV pictures.   If each of these pictures is equally likely, the probability of a given picture is $1/10^{300,000}$ and the amount of information provided by one such picture is†

$$I(E) = 300{,}000 \log 10$$
$$\approx 10^6 \text{ bits}$$

We may compare the information contained in one television picture calculated above with the information contained in 1,000 words from a radio announcer.   Let us assume that the announcer has a vocabulary of 10,000 words and that he selects 1,000 words from this vocabulary in a completely random fashion.   (It is possible to find radio announcers for whom this is a reasonable approximation.)   Then the probability of any one sequence of 1,000 words is $1/(10{,}000)^{1,000}$, and the amount of information provided is

$$I(E) = 1{,}000 \log 10{,}000$$
$$\approx 1.3 \times 10^4 \text{ bits}$$

Thus, a (TV) picture is, indeed, worth 1,000 (radio) words.

2-2. The Zero-memory Information Source

It will be useful to have available a mathematical description of an information-generating mechanism.   In this section, therefore,

---

† Henceforth, we shall write the logarithm to the base 2 of x simply as $\log x$, omitting the subscript 2 on the "log."   The natural logarithm of x will be written as $\ln x$.   All other logarithms will be indicated by displaying the base as a subscript (e.g., $\log_{10} x$).

we define a model of a discrete information source as shown in Figure 2-1.

We think of the source as emitting a sequence of symbols from a fixed finite source alphabet $S = \{s_1, s_2, \ldots, s_q\}$. Successive symbols are selected according to some fixed probability law. We shall occasionally refer to the source itself as S, but no confusion will be generated thereby. For the simplest kind of source, we

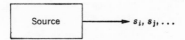

FIGURE 2-1. An information source.

assume that successive symbols emitted from the source are statistically independent. Such an information source is termed a *zero-memory source* and is completely described by the source alphabet S and the probabilities with which the symbols occur:

$$P(s_1), P(s_2), \ldots, P(s_q)$$

We may calculate the average information provided by a zero-memory information source as follows: If symbol s_i occurs, we obtain an amount of information equal to

$$I(s_i) = \log \frac{1}{P(s_i)} \quad \text{bits}$$

The probability that this will happen is just $P(s_i)$, so that the *average* amount of information obtained per symbol from the source is

$$\sum_S P(s_i)I(s_i) \quad \text{bits} \qquad \frac{1}{3} I(s_1) + \frac{2}{3} I(s_2) = \frac{I(s_1) + 2}{3}$$

where the $\sum\limits_S$ indicates a summation over the q symbols of the source S. This quantity, the average amount of information per source symbol, is called the *entropy* $H(S)$ of the zero-memory source.[†]

$$H(S) \triangleq \sum_S P(s_i) \log \frac{1}{P(s_i)} \quad \text{bits} \qquad (2\text{-}5a)$$

[†] The relation of the entropy of information theory to the entropy of statistical thermodynamics is discussed in Brillouin (1956).

Amnt of Info equivalent to amnt of uncertainty
as the larger the uncertainty the larger the Info
contained in message confirming the happening of that
uncertain event.

INFORMATION AND SOURCES   15

Example 2-1. Consider the source $S = \{s_1, s_2, s_3\}$ with $P(s_1) = \frac{1}{2}$ and $P(s_2) = P(s_3) = \frac{1}{4}$. Then

$$H(S) = \frac{1}{2} \log 2 + \frac{1}{4} \log 4 + \frac{1}{4} \log 4$$
$$= \frac{3}{2} \text{ bits}$$

If $I(s_i)$ is measured in r-ary units, then $H(S)$ is also measured in r-ary units, and we have

$$H_r(S) = \sum_S P(s_i) \log_r \frac{1}{P(s_i)} \qquad r\text{-ary units} \qquad (2\text{-}5b)$$

From Equation (2-2), we see that

average log value

average log value $\rightarrow H_r(S) = \dfrac{H(S)}{\log r}$ $\qquad\qquad\qquad (2\text{-}5c)$

Note that by the definition given in (2-1) we can interpret $I(s_i)$ as the information needed to make the occurrence of s_i certain. $H(S)$ then may be interpreted *either* as the average amount of information per symbol provided by the source *or* as the average amount of uncertainty which the observer has before his inspection of the output of the source. We shall make use of both these interpretations in the material which follows. First, however, we demonstrate some simple properties of the entropy of a source.

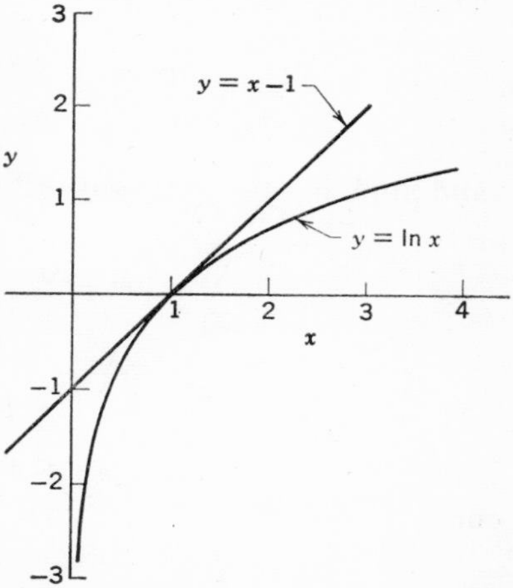

2-3. Some Properties of Entropy

In order to derive some properties of entropy, we shall have to make use of a property of the logarithm. The natural logarithm of x is sketched in Figure 2-2.

FIGURE 2-2. The natural logarithm of x, and $x - 1$.

Also sketched on the same set of axes is the line defined by the equation $y = x - 1$.

We may easily verify that the line $y = x - 1$ always lies above the curve $y = \ln x$. Thus we obtain the inequality

$$\ln x \leq x - 1 \tag{2-6}$$

with equality if, and only if, $x = 1$.

Multiplying (2-6) by -1, we obtain the additional inequality

$$\ln \frac{1}{x} \geq 1 - x \tag{2-7}$$

with equality if, and only if, $x = 1$.

Finally, we make use of (2-6) to obtain one further inequality. Let $x_1, x_2, \ldots, x_q$ and $y_1, y_2, \ldots, y_q$ be any two sets of probabilities. That is,

$$x_i \geq 0 \qquad y_j \geq 0 \qquad \text{for all } i \text{ and } j$$

and

$$\sum_{i=1}^{q} x_i = \sum_{j=1}^{q} y_j = 1$$

Then, using (2-2), we write

$$\sum_{i=1}^{q} x_i \log \frac{y_i}{x_i} = \frac{1}{\ln 2} \sum_{i=1}^{q} x_i \ln \frac{y_i}{x_i}$$

and applying the inequality (2-6) to each term in the sum,

$$\sum_{i=1}^{q} x_i \log \frac{y_i}{x_i} \leq \frac{1}{\ln 2} \sum_{i=1}^{q} x_i \left(\frac{y_i}{x_i} - 1 \right)$$

$$\leq \frac{1}{\ln 2} \left(\sum_{i=1}^{q} y_i - \sum_{i=1}^{q} x_i \right)$$

$$\leq 0 \tag{2-8a}$$

or

$$\sum_{i=1}^{q} x_i \log \frac{1}{x_i} \leq \sum_{i=1}^{q} x_i \log \frac{1}{y_i} \tag{2-8b}$$

with equality if, and only if, $x_i = y_i$ for all i.

As pointed out above, one possible interpretation of the entropy of a source is the average information per source symbol out of that source. It is quite natural, therefore, to investigate the manner in which the entropy depends upon the probabilities of the various source symbols. In particular, we should like to know how much information a zero-memory information source may give us.

Let a zero-memory information source with q symbols be defined by the source alphabet $S = \{s_i\}$, $i = 1, 2, \ldots, q$, and the probabilities $P(s_i) = P_i$, $i = 1, 2, \ldots, q$. Then $H(S)$ is given by

$$H(S) = \sum_{i=1}^{q} P_i \log \frac{1}{P_i} \qquad (2\text{-}9)$$

Consider the quantity

$$\log q - H(S) = \sum_{i=1}^{q} P_i \log q - \sum_{i=1}^{q} P_i \log \frac{1}{P_i}$$

$$= \sum_{i=1}^{q} P_i \log qP_i$$

$$= \log e \sum_{i=1}^{q} P_i \ln qP_i \qquad (2\text{-}10)$$

The last line is obtained using (2-2).   Now, we apply the inequality given in (2-7) to (2-10) and obtain

$$\log q - H(S) \geq \log e \sum_{i=1}^{q} P_i \left(1 - \frac{1}{qP_i}\right)$$

$$\geq \log e \left(\sum_{i=1}^{q} P_i - \frac{1}{q} \sum_{i=1}^{q} \frac{P_i}{P_i}\right)$$

$$\geq 0 \qquad (2\text{-}11)$$

Thus, $H(S)$ is always less than, or equal to, $\log q$.   Furthermore, the inequality was introduced at one point only, so that from the equality condition of (2-7) we see we shall have strict equality if, and only if, $P_i = 1/q$ for all i.   That is, we have shown that for a zero-memory information source with a q-symbol source alphabet, *the maximum value of the entropy is exactly log q, and this maximum value is achieved if, and only if, all the source symbols are equiprobable.*

One particularly important example of a zero-memory information source is the zero-memory binary source.   For such a source, the source alphabet S is just $\{0, 1\}$.   The probability of a 0 is ω

and the probability of a 1 is $1 - \omega$. We define $\bar{\omega} = 1 - \omega$. From (2-5) we may calculate the entropy of such a source,

$$H(S) = \omega \log \frac{1}{\omega} + \bar{\omega} \log \frac{1}{\bar{\omega}} \quad \text{bits} \qquad (2\text{-}12)$$

The function of ω given in (2-12) occurs frequently in information-theory problems. Accordingly, it is customary to assign a special symbol to this function. We define

$$H(\omega) = \omega \log \frac{1}{\omega} + \bar{\omega} \log \frac{1}{\bar{\omega}} \qquad (2\text{-}13)$$

and we call $H(\omega)$ the *entropy function*. Note the distinction between (2-12) and (2-13). $H(S)$ gives the entropy of a particular source S, while $H(\omega)$ is a function of the variable ω defined on [0, 1]. The meaning of the symbol $H(\cdot)$ is conveyed by its argument. Another point to note is that

$$\lim_{\omega \to 0} \omega \log \omega = 0$$

and so we define

$$0 \log 0 = 0$$

We have plotted $H(\omega)$ as a function of ω for ω in [0, 1] in Figure 2-3.

Note that if the output of this binary source is certain (either $\omega = 0$ or $\omega = 1$), then the source provides no information. The maximum average amount of information provided by each symbol of a binary source is log 2, or 1 bit; this occurs if, and only if, the 0 and 1 are equally likely.

The outputs of a binary source are binary digits or binits. Thus, we see that a sequence of binits from a zero-memory binary information source with equiprobable 0s and 1s will provide 1 bit of information per binit. If the 0s and 1s are not equally probable, then the amount of information provided by a given binit will be either less than or greater than 1 bit, depending upon its probability [cf. (2-1)]. The *average* amount of information provided by a binit from such a binary source, however, will always be less than or equal to 1 *bit* per *binit* (Figure 2-3).

It should be noted that the maximum amount of information provided by a zero-memory information source with q symbols increases slowly as q is increased.   In fact, the maximum amount of information provided by such a source increases only as the logarithm of the number of source symbols, and in order to double the maximum amount of information per symbol provided by a source with q symbols, we must use a source with q^2 symbols.

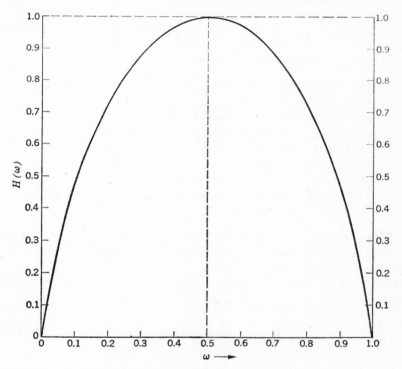

FIGURE 2-3. $H(\omega)$—the entropy function.

2-4. Extensions of a Zero-memory Source

In discussing the properties of information sources and information channels, in subsequent chapters we shall often find it useful to deal with blocks of symbols rather than individual symbols. For example, in the case of the binary source treated in the previous section we may think of the binits from the source as being emitted in groups of two.   The binary source considered in this manner is clearly equivalent to a source with four possible symbols—00, 01, 10, and 11. It is possible to extend this idea. If we think of our original binary source as emitting binits in groups of three, then, since there are eight possible binary sequences of length 3, the binary source considered in this manner is equivalent to a source with a source alphabet of eight symbols.

In general, if we have a zero-memory source S with source alphabet $\{s_1, s_2, \ldots, s_q\}$ we may consider the outputs of S taken n at a time. There are q^n such sequences of outputs. We formalize this natural notion in the following definition.

> *Definition.* Let S be a zero-memory information source with source alphabet $\{s_1, s_2, \ldots, s_q\}$ and with the probability of s_i equal to P_i. Then the nth extension of S, S^n, is a zero-memory source with q^n symbols $\{\sigma_1, \sigma_2, \ldots, \sigma_{q^n}\}$. Each σ_i corresponds to some sequence of n of the s_i. $P(\sigma_i)$, the probability of σ_i, is just the probability of the corresponding sequence of s_i's. That is, if σ_i corresponds to $(s_{i_1}, s_{i_2}, \ldots, s_{i_n})$, then $P(\sigma_i) = P_{i_1} P_{i_2} \cdots P_{i_n}$.

Since one symbol from S^n, the nth extension of the zero-memory source S, corresponds to n symbols from S, we expect† the entropy per symbol of S^n to be n times the entropy per symbol of S. This is not difficult to prove. Let σ_i be the symbol of S^n corresponding to the sequence $(s_{i_1}, s_{i_2}, \ldots, s_{i_n})$ of S. Then

$$H(S^n) = \sum_{S^n} P(\sigma_i) \log \frac{1}{P(\sigma_i)} \qquad (2\text{-}14)$$

where the summation is over the q^n symbols of S^n. When dealing with a source and its extensions, we shall use the notation $\sum_{S^n}$ to indicate a summation over all the symbols of the nth extension.

Such a summation over the q^n symbols of S^n is equivalent to n summations, each one over the q symbols of S. This is so since $\sigma_i = (s_{i_1}, s_{i_2}, \ldots, s_{i_n})$. For example, since $P(\sigma_i) = P_{i_1} P_{i_2} \cdots P_{i_n}$ for a zero-memory source,

† Note that, by our definition, the *first* extension of a source S is the source itself.

$$\sum_{S^n} P(\sigma_i) = \sum_{S^n} P_{i_1} P_{i_2} \cdots P_{i_n}$$

$$= \sum_{i_1=1}^{q} \sum_{i_2=1}^{q} \cdots \sum_{i_n=1}^{q} P_{i_1} P_{i_2} \cdots P_{i_n}$$

$$= \sum_{i_1=1}^{q} P_{i_1} \sum_{i_2=1}^{q} P_{i_2} \cdots \sum_{i_n=1}^{q} P_{i_n}$$

$$= 1 \tag{2-15}$$

Equation (2-14) may be written as

$$H(S^n) = \sum_{S^n} P(\sigma_i) \log \frac{1}{P_{i_1} P_{i_2} \cdots P_{i_n}}$$

$$= \sum_{S^n} P(\sigma_i) \log \frac{1}{P_{i_1}} + \sum_{S^n} P(\sigma_i) \log \frac{1}{P_{i_2}}$$

$$+ \cdots + \sum_{S^n} P(\sigma_i) \log \frac{1}{P_{i_n}} \tag{2-16}$$

If we take just the first term of the sum of summations given above, we see that we may perform $n - 1$ of the indicated summations,

$$\sum_{S^n} P(\sigma_i) \log \frac{1}{P_{i_1}} = \sum_{S^n} P_{i_1} P_{i_2} \cdots P_{i_n} \log \frac{1}{P_{i_1}}$$

$$= \sum_{i_1=1}^{q} P_{i_1} \log \frac{1}{P_{i_1}} \sum_{i_2=1}^{q} P_{i_2} \cdots \sum_{i_n=1}^{q} P_{i_n}$$

$$= \sum_{i_1=1}^{q} P_{i_1} \log \frac{1}{P_{i_1}}$$

$$= \sum_{S} P_{i_1} \log \frac{1}{P_{i_1}}$$

$$= H(S) \tag{2-17}$$

and using (2-17) to evaluate the other terms of (2-16), we obtain the desired result:

$$H(S^n) = nH(S) \tag{2-18}$$

Example 2-2. We take the second extension of the source of Example 2-1. Recall that this source had an alphabet $S = \{s_1, s_2, s_3\}$ with $P(s_1) = \frac{1}{2}$ and $P(s_2) = P(s_3) = \frac{1}{4}$. Then S^2 has nine symbols, as follows:

Symbols of S^2	σ_1	σ_2	σ_3	σ_4	σ_5	σ_6	σ_7	σ_8	σ_9
Corresponding sequence of S symbols	s_1s_1	s_1s_2	s_1s_3	s_2s_1	s_2s_2	s_2s_3	s_3s_1	s_3s_2	s_3s_3
Probability $P(\sigma_i)$	$\frac{1}{4}$	$\frac{1}{8}$	$\frac{1}{8}$	$\frac{1}{8}$	$\frac{1}{16}$	$\frac{1}{16}$	$\frac{1}{8}$	$\frac{1}{16}$	$\frac{1}{16}$

$$H(S^2) = \sum_{S^2} P(\sigma_i) \log \frac{1}{P(\sigma_i)}$$
$$= \tfrac{1}{4} \log 4 + 4 \times \tfrac{1}{8} \log 8 + 4 \times \tfrac{1}{16} \log 16$$
$$= 3 \text{ bits/symbol}$$

2-5. The Markov Information Source

The zero-memory source considered so far is too restrictive for some applications. A more general type of information source with q symbols than the zero-memory source already considered is one in which the occurrence of a source symbol s_i may depend upon a finite number m of preceding symbols. Such a source (called an mth-order Markov source) is specified by giving the source alphabet S and the set of conditional probabilities†

$$P(s_i/s_{j_1}, s_{j_2}, \ldots, s_{j_m}) \quad \text{for } i = 1, 2, \ldots, q; j_p = 1, 2, \ldots, q \tag{2-19}$$

For an mth-order Markov source, the probability of emitting a given symbol is known if we know the m preceding symbols. At any one time, therefore, we shall call the m preceding symbols the *state* of the mth-order Markov source at that time. Since there are q possible symbols, an mth-order Markov source will have q^m possible states. As symbols are emitted from the source, the state changes. A handy way to illustrate the behavior of a Markov source is through the use of a *state diagram*. In a state diagram we represent each of the q^m possible states of the source by a single point, and the possible transitions from state to state by arrows.

Example 2-3. Consider a second-order Markov source with the binary source alphabet $S = \{0, 1\}$. We assume the conditional symbol probabilities

$$P(0/00) = P(1/11) = 0.8$$
$$P(1/00) = P(0/11) = 0.2$$
$$P(0/01) = P(0/10) = P(1/01) = P(1/10) = 0.5$$

Because q is equal to 2 and we have assumed a *second*-order Markov source, we have *four* states of the source—00, 01, 10, 11. The state diagram for this

† The time sequence of symbols implied by the conditional probability $P(s_i/s_{j_1}, s_{j_2}, \ldots, s_{j_m})$ is $s_{j_1}, s_{j_2}, \ldots, s_{j_m}, s_i$. That is, s_i follows s_{j_m}.

source is shown in Figure 2-4. The possible states of our source are indicated by the four dots. The possible state transitions are indicated by arrows from state to state, with the probability of a transition shown by a number associated with each arrow. For example, if we are in state *00* we can go to either *01* or *00* but not to state *10* or *11*. The probability of remaining in state *00* is shown as 0.8, and the probability of going to state *01* is shown as 0.2.

In dealing with mth-order Markov information sources we shall restrict ourselves to the consideration of what are called *ergodic* sources. For the mathematician and for the mathematical statistician, the concept of ergodicity and the conditions under which a source is ergodic are somewhat involved. For our purposes, however, the concept of an ergodic source is simplicity itself. An

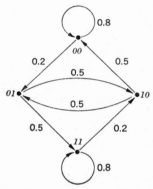

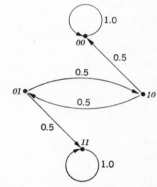

FIGURE 2-4. State diagram of a second-order Markov source.   FIGURE 2-5. State diagram of a nonergodic second-order Markov source.

ergodic source is merely a source which, if observed for a very long time, will (with probability 1) emit a sequence of source symbols which is "typical." In fact, the idea of sources possessing the ergodic property is so natural that some readers may have difficulty in picturing a source which is *not* ergodic. We therefore give an example of a *nonergodic* information source.

Example 2-4. Consider a second-order Markov source with the binary source alphabet $S = \{0, 1\}$. We assume the conditional symbol probabilities

$$P(0/00) = P(1/11) = 1.0$$
$$P(1/00) = P(0/11) = 0$$
$$P(0/01) = P(0/10) = P(1/01) = P(1/10) = 0.5$$

As in the previous example, we have four states—00, 01, 10, 11. The state diagram for this source is shown in Figure 2-5. Note that, for this source, if we ever arrive at either state *00* or *11*, we stay in that state forever. Furthermore, let us select one of the four possible states at random (i.e., each state has a probability of $\frac{1}{4}$ of being selected). Then, if we start in the state selected, we know that after a large number of state transitions have taken place, we will be in state *00* with probability 0.5. That is, after a large number of symbols have been emitted from the source, the source will emit a *0* with probability 0.5 and a *1* with probability 0.5. In any *given* sequence out of the source, however, if we wait a long time, we will almost surely see either *all* zeros or *all* ones. In other words (with probability 1) we will not see a typical sequence from this source; it is not ergodic.

The discussion given above points out the difficulty, from our point of view, with nonergodic sources. If we select the initial state of a Markov source (according to some set of initial probabilities over the states) and wait a large number of state transitions, we know that there will be some definite probability with which each of the states will occur. Furthermore, as suggested by our use of the word *typical* in the previous paragraph, for an ergodic source the states which actually do appear in a very long sequence will (with probability 1) occur with these same probabilities. It is a further remarkable property of ergodic Markov sources (Feller, 1950) that the probability distribution over the set of states which appears after many state transitions (or, equivalently, the distribution of states in a typical output sequence) does *not* depend upon the initial distribution with which the states are chosen. There is a unique probability distribution over the set of states of an *ergodic* Markov source, and the states in any long output sequence will (with probability 1) occur with this distribution. This unique probability distribution is called the *stationary distribution* of the ergodic Markov process; *since the stationary distribution does not depend upon the initial distribution with which the states are chosen, it can be calculated from the conditional symbol probabilities alone.* For example, for the Markov source given in Figure 2-4 it is possible to show that the stationary distribution is

$$P(00) = P(11) = \tfrac{5}{14}$$
$$P(01) = P(10) = \tfrac{2}{14} \qquad (2\text{-}20)$$

When we specify the conditional symbol probabilities $P(s_i/s_{j_1}, s_{j_2}, \ldots, s_{j_m})$ of an ergodic mth-order Markov process, we also implicitly specify the q^m state probabilities $P(s_{j_1}, s_{j_2}, \ldots, s_{j_m})$. Upon combining these two probabilities, we obtain the probability of the *joint event* "the source is in the state specified by $(s_{j_1}, s_{j_2}, \ldots, s_{j_m})$ and s_i occurs." This probability is just

$$P(s_{j_1}, s_{j_2}, \ldots, s_{j_m}, s_i) = P(s_i/s_{j_1}, s_{j_2}, \ldots, s_{j_m})P(s_{j_1}, s_{j_2}, \ldots, s_{j_m}) \tag{2-21}$$

It should be noted that we have not discussed the problem of actually calculating the state probabilities of an ergodic Markov source, given the conditional source probabilities. This is, in general, a difficult task, and the reader is referred to Feller (1950) or Bharucha-Reid (1960) for details. All we make use of is the fact that the state probabilities *may* be calculated from a knowledge of the conditional symbol probabilities.

We may calculate the average information provided by an mth-order Markov source† as follows: If we are in the state specified by $(s_{j_1}, s_{j_2}, \ldots, s_{j_m})$ (i.e., the m previous symbols emitted were $s_{j_1}, s_{j_2}, \ldots, s_{j_m}$), then the conditional probability of receiving symbol s_i is $P(s_i/s_{j_1}, s_{j_2}, \ldots, s_{j_m})$. From (2-1) the information we obtain if s_i occurs while we are in state $(s_{j_1}, s_{j_2}, \ldots, s_{j_m})$ is

$$I(s_i/s_{j_1}, s_{j_2}, \ldots, s_{j_m}) = \log \frac{1}{P(s_i/s_{j_1}, s_{j_2}, \ldots, s_{j_m})} \tag{2-22}$$

Therefore, the average amount of information per symbol *while we are in state* $(s_{j_1}, s_{j_2}, \ldots, s_{j_m})$ is given in Equation (2-23):

$$H(S/s_{j_1}, s_{j_2}, \ldots, s_{j_m})$$
$$= \sum_S P(s_i/s_{j_1}, s_{j_2}, \ldots, s_{j_m})I(s_i/s_{j_1}, s_{j_2}, \ldots, s_{j_m}) \tag{2-23}$$

If we average this quantity over the q^m possible states, we obtain the average amount of information, or the entropy of the mth-order Markov source S.

$$H(S) = \sum_{S^m} P(s_{j_1}, s_{j_2}, \ldots, s_{j_m})H(S/s_{j_1}, s_{j_2}, \ldots, s_{j_m}) \tag{2-24a}$$

In writing (2-24a), we have used the fact that the state $(s_{j_1}, s_{j_2}, \ldots, s_{j_m})$ is equivalent to a symbol‡ from S^m. Using (2-23) in

---

† Henceforth we shall omit the word *ergodic* when discussing such sources. The remainder of this book will treat only the ergodic case.

‡ Strictly speaking, we have not yet defined S^m, the mth extension of a *Markov* source S. The use of S^m in (2-24), however, is unambiguous. The complete definition of an extension of a Markov source is given in Section 2-7.

(2-24a), we obtain

$$H(S) = \sum_{S^m} P(s_{j_1}, s_{j_2}, \ldots, s_{j_m}) \sum_{S} P(s_i/s_{j_1}, s_{j_2}, \ldots, s_{j_m})$$

$$\times \log \frac{1}{P(s_i/s_{j_1}, s_{j_2}, \ldots, s_{j_m})}$$

$$= \sum_{S^{m+1}} P(s_{j_1}, s_{j_2}, \ldots, s_{j_m}) P(s_i/s_{j_1}, s_{j_2}, \ldots, s_{j_m})$$

$$\times \log \frac{1}{P(s_i/s_{j_1}, s_{j_2}, \ldots, s_{j_m})}$$

$$= \sum_{S^{m+1}} P(s_{j_1}, s_{j_2}, \ldots, s_{j_m}, s_i)$$

$$\times \log \frac{1}{P(s_i/s_{j_1}, s_{j_2}, \ldots, s_{j_m})} \qquad (2\text{-}24b)$$

where (2-21) was used in the last step.

Note that if S is zero-memory rather than Markov,

$$P(s_i/s_{j_1}, s_{j_2}, \ldots, s_{j_m}) = P(s_i)$$

and (2-24b) reduces to (2-5a).

Example 2-5. We consider the Markov source of Figure 2-4. The stationary distribution of this source is given in (2-20). The relevant probabilities are summarized in Table 2-1.

TABLE 2-1. PROBABILITIES FOR THE MARKOV SOURCE OF FIGURE 2-4

s_j, s_k, s_i	$P(s_i/s_j, s_k)$	$P(s_j, s_k)$	$P(s_j, s_k, s_i)$
000	0.8	$\frac{5}{14}$	$\frac{4}{14}$
001	0.2	$\frac{5}{14}$	$\frac{1}{14}$
010	0.5	$\frac{2}{14}$	$\frac{1}{14}$
011	0.5	$\frac{2}{14}$	$\frac{1}{14}$
100	0.5	$\frac{2}{14}$	$\frac{1}{14}$
101	0.5	$\frac{2}{14}$	$\frac{1}{14}$
110	0.2	$\frac{5}{14}$	$\frac{1}{14}$
111	0.8	$\frac{5}{14}$	$\frac{4}{14}$

Then the entropy is calculated using (2-24b):

$$H(S) = \sum_{S^3} P(s_j, s_k, s_i) \log \frac{1}{P(s_i/s_j, s_k)}$$

$$= 2 \times \tfrac{4}{14} \log \frac{1}{0.8} + 2 \times \tfrac{1}{14} \log \frac{1}{0.2} + 4 \times \tfrac{1}{14} \log \frac{1}{0.5}$$

$$= 0.81 \text{ bit/binit}$$

2-6. The Adjoint Source

If we are given an mth-order Markov source, we may, in principle, calculate the stationary distribution—the distribution of states of the Markov source. For a *first-order* Markov source, the set of states is identical with the set of source symbols, and the stationary distribution gives us the first-order (unconditional) probability distribution of source symbols directly. For a higher-order Markov source, the first-order probability distribution of source symbols may be obtained from the stationary distribution with little additional effort. The Markov source with stationary distribution given in (2-20), for example, may be shown to have the first-order symbol probabilities $P(0) = P(1) = \frac{1}{2}$. Using the first-order symbol probabilities of a Markov source, we may define another source.

> *Definition.* Let $S = \{s_1, s_2, \ldots, s_q\}$ be the source alphabet of an mth-order Markov source, and let $P_1, P_2, \ldots, P_q$ be the first-order symbol probabilities of the source. The *adjoint source* to S, written $\bar{S}$, is the zero-memory information source with source alphabet identical with that of S, and with symbol probabilities $P_1, P_2, \ldots, P_q$.

For example, by the symmetry of the state diagram shown in Figure 2-4, 0 and 1 are equally probable. Thus, the adjoint of the source of Figure 2-4 is a zero-memory binary source with equiprobable input symbols and $H(\bar{S}) = 1$. Note that the adjoint of a *zero-memory* source S is just S itself. We shall show that the entropy of the adjoint source $\bar{S}$ is never less than the entropy of S. This fact has an important interpretation. The two sources S and $\bar{S}$ have identical first-order symbol probabilities. They differ only in the fact that S has additional constraints expressed in terms of *conditional* symbol probabilities imposed on its output sequences. These constraints, therefore, serve to decrease the average amount of information flowing out of the source.

In order to simplify the notation, we shall prove that $H(\bar{S})$ is greater than or equal to $H(S)$ when S is a *first-order* Markov source. The corresponding proof for the mth-order Markov source is a direct extension.

Let S be a first-order Markov source with symbols $s_1, s_2, \ldots, s_q$

and conditional symbol probabilities $P(s_i/s_j)$, $i, j = 1, 2, \ldots, q$. Let $P_1, P_2, \ldots, P_q$ be the first-order symbol probabilities of S, and let $\bar{S}$ be the adjoint source. If we define $P(s_j, s_i)$ as the joint probability that the source is in the state specified by s_j, and s_i occurs, we may write [corresponding to (2-21)]

$$P(s_j, s_i) = P(s_i/s_j)P_j \tag{2-25}$$

Now we examine the double summation

$$\sum_{S^2} P(s_j, s_i) \log \frac{P_j P_i}{P(s_j, s_i)} \tag{2-26}$$

From (2-8a) we see that this summation is less than or equal to 0, with equality if and only if

$$P(s_j, s_i) = P_j P_i \qquad \text{for all } i \text{ and } j \tag{2-27}$$

Upon combining (2-25) and (2-26) and writing the inequality, we have

$$\sum_{S^2} P(s_j, s_i) \log \frac{P_i}{P(s_i/s_j)} \leq 0$$

or

$$\sum_{S^2} P(s_j, s_i) \log \frac{1}{P(s_i/s_j)} \leq \sum_{S^2} P(s_j, s_i) \log \frac{1}{P_i}$$

$$\leq \sum_{i=1}^{q} \sum_{j=1}^{q} P(s_j, s_i) \log \frac{1}{P_i} \tag{2-28}$$

The summation over the index j of the double summation on the right may be performed immediately by noting that the logarithm is independent of j and that

$$\sum_{j=1}^{q} P(s_j, s_i) = P_i$$

so that we get

$$\sum_{S^2} P(s_j, s_i) \log \frac{1}{P(s_i/s_j)} \leq \sum_{S} P_i \log \frac{1}{P_i}$$

or

$$H(S) \leq H(\bar{S}) \tag{2-29}$$

The condition for equality [expressed in (2-27)] is simply that s_i and s_j are statistically independent, i.e., that S is really a zero-memory source. We have already seen one example of the relation expressed in (2-29). Recall that, for the Markov source of Figure 2-4, $H(S) = 0.81$ bit while $H(\bar{S}) = 1$ bit.

2-7. Extensions of a Markov Source

In Section 2-4 we defined an extension of a zero-memory source. An extension of a Markov source may be defined in a similar manner by considering blocks of n symbols from the source as comprising a new symbol σ_i.

> *Definition.* Let S be an mth-order Markov information source with source alphabet $(s_1, s_2, \ldots, s_q)$ and conditional symbol probabilities $P(s_i/s_{j_1}, s_{j_2}, \ldots, s_{j_m})$. Then the nth extension of S, S^n, is a μth-order Markov source with q^n symbols, $\sigma_1, \sigma_2, \ldots, \sigma_{q^n}$. Each σ_i corresponds to some sequence of n of the s_i, and the conditional symbol probabilities of σ_i are $P(\sigma_i/\sigma_{j_1}, \sigma_{j_2}, \ldots, \sigma_{j_\mu})$. The definitions of these probabilities and of μ are given directly below.

In order to describe completely the statistics of the nth extension of an mth-order Markov source, we must specify the conditional probabilities

$$P(\sigma_i/s_{j_1}, s_{j_2}, \ldots, s_{j_m}) \tag{2-30}$$

where σ_i represents a symbol of the nth extension—a sequence of n symbols s_i. The sequence $(s_{j_1}, s_{j_2}, \ldots, s_{j_m})$ is equivalent to some sequence of σ_i, say $\sigma_{j_1}, \sigma_{j_2}, \ldots, \sigma_{j_\mu}$, where $\mu = [m/n]$, the smallest integer greater than or equal to m/n.

The conditional symbol probabilities of (2-30), therefore, can be written as

$$P(\sigma_i/\sigma_{j_1}, \sigma_{j_2}, \ldots, \sigma_{j_\mu}) \tag{2-31}$$

For example, the third extension of a fifth-order Markov source with q symbols would be a second-order Markov source with q^3 symbols. Note that by taking at least m extensions of an mth-order Markov source we can always obtain a *first-order* Markov source. Finally, we produce an expression for $P(\sigma_i/\sigma_{j_1}, \sigma_{j_2}, \ldots, \sigma_{j_\mu})$ in terms

of the conditional symbol probabilities of the original source S.
Let $\sigma_i = (s_{i_1}, s_{i_2}, \ldots, s_{i_n})$. Then

$$P(\sigma_i/\sigma_{j_1}, \sigma_{j_2}, \ldots, \sigma_{j_\mu}) = P(s_{i_1}, s_{i_2}, \ldots, s_{i_n}/s_{j_1}, s_{j_2}, \ldots, s_{j_m})$$
$$= P(s_{i_1}/s_{j_1}, s_{j_2}, \ldots, s_{j_m})P(s_{i_2}/s_{j_2}, s_{j_3}, \ldots, s_{j_m}, s_{i_1})$$
$$\cdots P(s_{i_n}/s_{i_{n-m}}, s_{i_{n-m+1}}, \ldots, s_{i_{n-1}})$$

$$(2\text{-}32)$$

The form of the last term in the product assumes that $n > m$.
If $n \leq m$, the last term would be $P(s_{i_n}/s_{j_n}, s_{j_{n+1}}, \ldots, s_{i_{n-1}})$.

The entropy of the nth extension of a zero-memory source has
been shown to be n times the entropy of the original source. It is
easy to show that this property also holds for Markov sources.
Again we carry out the proof for the case of a first-order Markov
source.

Let S be a first-order Markov source with source alphabet
$\{s_1, s_2, \ldots, s_q\}$, transition probabilities $P(s_i/s_j)$, and stationary
distribution $P_1, P_2, \ldots, P_q$. Let S^n be the nth extension of S
with symbols σ_i, $i = 1, 2, \ldots, q^n$. S^n is a first-order Markov
source (by our definition of μ).

$$H(S^n) = \sum_{S^n} \sum_{S^n} P(\sigma_j, \sigma_i) \log \frac{1}{P(\sigma_i/\sigma_j)} \qquad (2\text{-}33a)$$

The right side of (2-33a), when viewed in terms of the source S^n,
is a double summation with both i and j running from 1 to q^n.
Alternatively, we may think of these summations in terms of the
$2n$th extension of the original source S. In this case,

$$H(S^n) = \sum_{S^{2n}} P(\sigma_j, \sigma_i) \log \frac{1}{P(\sigma_i/\sigma_j)} \qquad (2\text{-}33b)$$

Rewriting (2-32) for the case $m = 1$, we find

$$P(\sigma_i/\sigma_j) = P(s_{i_1}, s_{i_2}, \ldots, s_{i_n}/s_j)$$
$$= P(s_{i_1}/s_j)P(s_{i_2}/s_{i_1}) \cdots P(s_{i_n}/s_{i_{n-1}}) \qquad (2\text{-}34)$$

and the right side of (2-33b) may be separated into n summations:

$$H(S^n) = \sum_{S^{2n}} P(\sigma_j, \sigma_i) \log \frac{1}{P(s_{i_1}/s_j)} + \cdots$$
$$+ \sum_{S^{2n}} P(\sigma_j, \sigma_i) \log \frac{1}{P(s_{i_n}/s_{i_{n-1}})} \qquad (2\text{-}35)$$

Each of these summations may be reduced. For example, by performing $2n - 2$ of the indicated summations on the first term,

$$\sum_{S^{2n}} P(\sigma_j, \sigma_i) \log \frac{1}{P(s_{i_1}/s_j)} = \sum_{S^2} P(s_j, s_{i_1}) \log \frac{1}{P(s_{i_1}/s_j)}$$

$$= H(S) \qquad (2\text{-}36)$$

Hence

$$H(S^n) = nH(S) \qquad (2\text{-}37)$$

Further interesting properties of the entropy of a Markov source may be obtained by considering $\overline{S^n}$, the adjoint of S^n. Let $P(\sigma_1)$, $P(\sigma_2)$, . . . , $P(\sigma_{q^n})$ be the first-order symbol probabilities of the σ_i, the symbols of the nth extension of the first-order Markov source considered above. Since σ_i corresponds to the sequence $(s_{i_1}, s_{i_2}, . . . , s_{i_n})$, we see that $P(\sigma_i)$ may also be thought of as the nth-order joint probability of the s_{i_k}.

$$H(\overline{S^n}) = \sum_{S^n} P(\sigma_i) \log \frac{1}{P(\sigma_i)}$$

$$= \sum_{S^n} P(s_{i_1}, s_{i_2}, . . . , s_{i_n}) \log \frac{1}{P(s_{i_1}, s_{i_2}, . . . , s_{i_n})} \qquad (2\text{-}38)$$

S is a *first-order* Markov source, however, so that

$$P(s_{i_1}, s_{i_2}, . . . , s_{i_n}) = P(s_{i_1})P(s_{i_2}/s_{i_1}) \cdots (s_{i_n}/s_{i_{n-1}}) \qquad (2\text{-}39)$$

Putting (2-39) into (2-38), we obtain

$$H(\overline{S^n}) = \sum_{S^n} P(s_{i_1}, s_{i_2}, . . . , s_{i_n}) \left[\log \frac{1}{P(s_{i_1})} + \log \frac{1}{P(s_{i_2}/s_{i_1})} \right.$$

$$\left. + \cdots + \log \frac{1}{P(s_{i_n}/s_{i_{n-1}})} \right]$$

$$= H(\bar{S}) + (n - 1)H(S) \qquad (2\text{-}40)$$

or

$$H(\overline{S^n}) = nH(S) + [H(\bar{S}) - H(S)] \qquad (2\text{-}41)$$

Note that the term in the brackets on the right side of (2-41) is a nonnegative constant, independent of n. If S is an mth-order (rather than just a first-order) Markov source, then (2-41) must be replaced by

$$H(\overline{S^n}) = nH(S) + \epsilon_m \qquad (2\text{-}42)$$

where ϵ_m is a positive constant which (as long as $n > m$) depends only upon the statistics of S (Problem 2-1).

If we divide both sides of (2-42) by n, we find

$$\frac{H(\overline{S^n})}{n} = H(S) + \frac{\epsilon_m}{n} \tag{2-43}$$

We have previously seen (2-29) that

$$H(\overline{S^n}) \geq H(S^n) = nH(S) \tag{2-44}$$

Equation (2-43), however, tells us that this inequality becomes less important as n becomes larger. More precisely, from (2-43), we have

$$\lim_{n \to \infty} \frac{H(\overline{S^n})}{n} = H(S) \tag{2-45}$$

In other words, for large n, the Markov constraints on the symbols from S^n become less and less important.

A word of caution may be appropriate at this point. The adjoint of the nth extension of S is *not* the same as the nth extension of the adjoint of S.

$$H(\overline{S^n}) \neq H(\bar{S}^n) \tag{2-46}$$

In fact, since $\bar{S}$ is a zero-memory source,

$$H(\bar{S}^n) = nH(\bar{S}) \tag{2-47}$$

which may be contrasted with (2-44).

Example 2-6. We may collect some results given in previous examples dealing with the source of Figure 2-4 to illustrate the preceding equations. We have obtained

$$H(S) = 0.81 \text{ bit}$$
$$H(\bar{S}) = 1.00 \text{ bit}$$

From (2-37),

$$H(S^2) = 2H(S) = 1.62 \text{ bits}$$

We can calculate

$$H(\overline{S^2}) = \sum_{S^2} P(s_j, s_k) \log \frac{1}{P(s_j, s_k)}$$
$$= 1.86 \text{ bits}$$

Even more tedious calculations yield

$$H(\overline{S^3}) = 2.66 \text{ bits}$$
$$H(\overline{S^4}) = 3.47 \text{ bits}$$

Note how the sequence

$$H(\bar{S}) = 1.00 \text{ bit}$$

$$\frac{H(\overline{S^2})}{2} = 0.93 \text{ bit}$$

$$\frac{H(\overline{S^3})}{3} = 0.89 \text{ bit}$$

$$\frac{H(\overline{S^4})}{4} = 0.87 \text{ bit}$$

approaches $H(S)$.

2-8. The Structure of Language

In the previous sections of this chapter, we have defined a model of an information source, and brought out some simple properties of our model. It is of some interest to investigate how closely such a model approximates the physical process of information generation. A particularly important case of information generation is the generation of a message composed of English words. In this section we show how the generation of such a message may be approximated by a sequence of successively more and more complicated information sources.

Let us restrict ourselves to a set of 27 symbols—the 26 English letters and a space. The simplest possible source using this alphabet is a zero-memory source with all 27 symbols equally probable. The entropy of this source is easily calculated.

$$H(S) = \log 27$$
$$= 4.75 \text{ bits/symbol} \tag{2-48}$$

A typical sequence of symbols emitted by such a source is shown in Figure 2-6. We refer to this sequence as the zeroth approximation to English.

ZEWRTZYNSADXESYJRQY—WGECIJJ—OBVKRBQPOZB
YMBUAWVLBTQCNIKFMP—KMVUUGBSAXHLHSIE—M

FIGURE 2-6. Zeroth approximation to English.

Note that there is no perceptible structure to this sequence and it is not possible to identify it as coming from any particular language using the same alphabet. A better approximation to English may be obtained by employing the actual probabilities

of the symbols used (Table 2-2). The entropy of a zero-memory
source with probabilities given in Table 2-2 is

$$H(S) = \sum_{S} P_i \log \frac{1}{P_i}$$

$$= 4.03 \text{ bits/symbol} \tag{2-49}$$

TABLE 2-2. PROBABILITIES OF SYMBOLS IN ENGLISH (REZA, 1961)

Symbol	Probability	Symbol	Probability
Space	0.1859	N	0.0574
A	0.0642	O	0.0632
B	0.0127	P	0.0152
C	0.0218	Q	0.0008
D	0.0317	R	0.0484
E	0.1031	S	0.0514
F	0.0208	T	0.0796
G	0.0152	U	0.0228
H	0.0467	V	0.0083
I	0.0575	W	0.0175
J	0.0008	X	0.0013
K	0.0049	Y	0.0164
L	0.0321	Z	0.0005
M	0.0198		

A typical sequence of symbols emitted by this source is given in
Figure 2-7.

AI_NGAE_ _ITF_NNR_ASAEV_OIE_BAINTHA_HYR
OO_POER_SETRYGAIETRWCO_ _EHDUARU_EU_C_F
T_NSREM_DIY_EESE_ _F_O_SRIS_R_ _UNNASHOR

FIGURE 2-7. First approximation to English.

Though the sequence shown here cannot qualify as good English,
it does exhibit some of the structure of the language. (Compare
this with our zeroth approximation.)   The "words" of this approximation are, for the most part, of reasonable length, and the proportion of vowels to consonants seems more realistic.   We may
improve upon the source which generated the first approximation
by using a first-order *Markov* source with the appropriate condi-

tional symbol probabilities.   These probabilities are given by Pratt (1942).

$$H(S) = \sum_{S^2} P(i, j) \log \frac{1}{P(i/j)}$$

$$= 3.32 \text{ bits/symbol} \qquad (2\text{-}50)$$

It is possible to generate a typical sequence of symbols out of such a first-order Markov source by using the probabilities given in Pratt. Shannon, however, has pointed out a much cleverer method.   Ordinary English text has the probabilities we seek contained in it. We therefore open a book and select a letter at random, say U. Next, we skip a few lines, read until we come to the first U and select the first letter after the U—in this case it was R.   Again we skip a few lines, read until we come to an R, and select the next letter.   Using this procedure, we constructed a second approximation to English (Figure 2-8).

URTESHETHING__AD__E__AT__FOULE__ITHALIORT__W
ACT__D__STE__MINTSAN__OLINS__TWID__OULY__TE__T
HIGHE__CO__YS__TH__HR__UPAVIDE__PAD__CTAVED

FIGURE 2-8. Second approximation to English.

Note how the English flavor of the sequence makes itself felt in the second approximation.   We would have little trouble in identifying this sequence as an approximation to English rather than, say, French.

We can apply Shannon's method to construct even better approximations to English.   By selecting letters from a book according to the *two* preceding letters we can construct a typical sequence from a second-order Markov source approximating English.

IANKS__CAN__OU__ANG__RLER__THATTED__OF__TO__S
HOR__OF__TO__HAVEMEM__A__I__MAND__AND__BUT__
WHISSITABLY__THERVEREER__EIGHTS__TAKILLIS__TA

FIGURE 2-9. Third approximation to English.

Shannon (1951) has estimated the entropy of the source corresponding to the sequence shown in Figure 2-9 as 3.1 bits per symbol. Using other methods, he has estimated that the entropy of English, taking into account all the preceding text, is between 0.6 and 1.3 bits per symbol.

It is possible to extend the process used above to generate typical sequences out of mth-order ($m \geq 3$) Markov sources having the symbol probabilities of English.   The construction of such sequences, however, becomes impractical for m greater than 2. Instead Shannon jumped to a zero-memory information source with the English *words* rather than the English letters as the output symbols.   The probabilities of occurrence of the various words are approximately the same as in English text.   Shannon (1948) obtained the approximation shown in Figure 2-10.

REPRESENTING   AND   SPEEDILY   IS   AN   GOOD   APT
OR   COME   CAN   DIFFERENT   NATURAL   HERE   HE
THE   A   IN   CAME   THE   TO   OF   TO   EXPERT
GRAY   COME   TO   FURNISHES   THE   LINE   MES-
SAGE   HAD   BE   THESE

FIGURE 2-10. Fourth approximation to English.

An even more complicated approximation to English can be constructed by letting the probability that a given word is selected depend upon one preceding word.   The source corresponding to this approximation is a first-order Markov source with the English words as symbols.   Shannon (1948) also constructed a typical sequence from this type of source (Figure 2-11).

THE   HEAD   AND   IN   FRONTAL   ATTACK   ON   AN
ENGLISH   WRITER   THAT   THE   CHARACTER   OF
THIS   POINT   IS   THEREFORE   ANOTHER   METHOD
FOR   THE   LETTERS   THAT   THE   TIME   OF   WHO
EVER   TOLD   THE   PROBLEM   FOR   AN   UNEX-
PECTED

FIGURE 2-11. Fifth approximation to English.

It is interesting to note that this sequence is a reasonable approximation to the sort of output one might expect from a very excited and quite incoherent speaker.   The fact that we can approximate (at least to some extent) as complicated an information source as an English speaker by the simple models of zero-memory and Markov sources is encouraging.   Many information sources found in realistic communication problems are of a much simpler nature, and we may expect that our models provide better approximations to reality in those cases.

A striking illustration of the differences in several Western languages may be obtained by constructing sequences using the statistics of these languages.   We have done this for three languages, and the sequences obtained are given in Figures 2-12 to 2-14.   As before, the first approximation corresponds to a sequence out of a zero-memory source; the second approximation from a first-order Markov source; and the third approximation from a second-order Markov source.

R__EPTTFVSIEOISETE__TTLGNSSSNLN__UNST__FSNST
F__E__IONIOILECMPADINMEC__TCEREPTTFLLUMGLR
ADBIUVDCMSFUAISRPMLGAVEAI__MILLUO

(a) First approximation to French

ITEPONT__JENE__IESEMANT__PAVEZ__L__BO__S__PAS
E__LQU__SUIN__DOTI__CIS__NC__MOUROUNENT__FUI
T__JE__DABREZ__DAUIETOUNT__LAGAUVRSOUT__MY

(b) Second approximation to French

JOU__MOUPLAS__DE__MONNERNAISSAINS__DEME__U
S__VREH__BRE__TU__DE__TOUCHEUR__DIMMERE__LL
ES__MAR__ELAME__RE__A__VER__IL__DOUVENTS__SO

(c) Third approximation to French

FIGURE 2-12. A series of approximations to French.

NNBNNDOETTNIIIAD__TSI__ISLEENS__LRI__LDRRBNF
REMTDEEIKE__U__HBF__EVSN__BRGANWN__IENEEHM
EN__RHN__LHD__SRG__EITAW__EESRNNCLGR

(a) First approximation to German

AFERORERGERAUSCHTER__DEHABAR__ADENDERG
E__E__UBRNDANAGR__ETU__ZUBERKLIN__DIMASO
N__DEU__UNGER__EIEIEMMLILCHER__WELT__WIERK

(b) Second approximation to German

BET__EREINER__SOMMEIT__SINACH__GAN__TURHATT
ER__AUM__WIE__BEST__ALLIENDER__TAUSSICHELLE
__LAUFURCHT__ER__BLEINDESEIT__UBER__KONN__

(c) Third approximation to German

FIGURE 2-13. A series of approximations to German.

UOALNAO__NEL__D__NIS__ETR__TEGATUEOEC__S__ASU
DU__ZELNNTSSCASOSED__T__I__R__EIS__TAMMO__TII
UOEDEO__UEI__EOSEELA__NMSLAANTEC
(a) First approximation to Spanish

CINDEUNECO__PE__CAL__PROS__E__LAS__LABITEJAS,
TE__ONTOMECITRODRESIO__PAY__EN__SPUSEL__LA
__S__UTAJARETES__OLONDAMIVE__ESA__S__CLUS__
(b) Second approximation to Spanish

RAMA__DE__LLA__EL__GUIA__IMO__SUS__CONDIAS__S
U__E__UNCONDADADO__DEA__MARE__TO__BUERBALI
A__NUE__Y__HERARSIN__DE__SE__SUS__SUPAROCEDA
(c) Third approximation to Spanish

FIGURE 2-14. A series of approximations to Spanish.

As a final example in this series, we present a series of approximations (Figure 2-15) to another Western language and leave it to the
reader to determine which language.

SETIOSTT__NINN__TUEEHHIUTIAUE__N__IREAISRI__M
INRNEMOSEPIN__MAIPSAC__SES__LN__ANEIISUNTINU
__AR__TM__UMOECNU__RIREIAL__AEFIITP
(a) First approximation to ?

CT__QU__VENINLUM__UA__QUREO__ABIT__SAT__FIUMA
GE__ICAM__MESTAM__M__QUM__CUTAT__PAM__NOND
QUM__O__M__FIT__NISERIST__E__L__ONO__IHOSEROCO
(b) Second approximation to ?

ET__LIGERCUM__SITECI__LIBEMUS__ACERELEN__TE
__VICAESCERUM__PE__NON__SUM__MINUS__UTERNE
__UT__IN__ARION__POPOMIN__SE__INQUENEQUE__IRA
(c) Third approximation to ?

FIGURE 2-15. A series of approximations to ?

NOTES

Note 1.   The word *entropy* was coined by Clausius in 1876 from the Greek
words εν and τρέπειν.   Together these words imply a "turning in."   Clausius
used entropy to denote that part of the energy of a system which cannot be
transformed into mechanical work without the transmission of heat to some
other body, or a change in volume.   Boltzmann, in 1896, was the first to show
that the entropy of a system could be expressed in terms of the average value

of the logarithm of the probabilities of the states of the system. Shannon (1948) introduced the word into information theory.

Entropy is certainly the most important but not the only point of contact between information theory and statistical mechanics. Jaynes (1959) discussed the use of the *partition function* of statistical mechanics in information theory.

Note 2. Throughout this book we assume that the symbol probabilities of the sources we treat are known. When these probabilities are unknown (and perhaps even the *number* of source symbols is unknown), we may wish to estimate the entropy of a zero-memory source from an observation of k outputs of that source. Miller and Madow (1954) find the maximum-likelihood estimate of the entropy based on such an observation.

Basharin (1959) uses the experimental probabilities $\hat{p}_i$ to form the natural estimate

$$\hat{H}(S) = \sum_S \hat{p}_i \log \frac{1}{\hat{p}_i}$$

He shows that $\hat{H}(S)$ is a biased, consistent, asymptotically normal estimate of $H(S)$ with

$$E[\hat{H}(S)] = H(S) - \frac{q-1}{2N} \log e + 0\left(\frac{1}{N^2}\right)$$

where q is the number of symbols of the source alphabet and N is the sample size of the observation. Blyth (1958) investigates certain other estimates of $H(S)$ and, in addition, shows that there exists no unbiased estimate of $H(S)$.

Note 3. In Section 2-2 we define the entropy of a random variable which can assume one of a finite number of values. (The distribution function of the random variable consists of a finite number of steps.)

In order to treat a random variable s which can assume values in some continuum (e.g., its distribution function is absolutely continuous), we might consider a sequence of finite-step distribution functions approximating the absolutely continuous distribution function. Let $[s]$ denote the integer part of s. Define the new random variable

$$s_n = \frac{1}{n} [ns]$$

and let

$$P_{nk} = \text{Pr}\left\{s_n = \frac{k}{n}\right\}$$

Let the source corresponding to the random variable s_n be S_n. As n increases, the random variable s_n resembles s more and more. Unfortunately $H(S_n)$ does not remain finite!

Renyi (1959) defined the *dimension* of the random variable s as

$$d(s) = \lim_{n \to \infty} \frac{H(S_n)}{\log n}$$

and the *d-dimensional entropy* of s as

$$H_d(S) = \lim_{n \to \infty} [H(S_n) - d \log n]$$

when these quantities exist.   When the distribution function consists of a finite number of steps, the dimension is clearly zero and $H_0(S)$ reduces to $H(S)$. Renyi (1959) shows that, when the distribution function is absolutely continuous and $H(S_1)$ is finite, $d(s) = 1$, and [letting $p(s)$ be the density function]

$$H_1(S) = \int_{-\infty}^{\infty} p(s) \log \frac{1}{p(s)} \, ds$$

if this integral exists.   Csiszar (1961) provides a partial converse to these results.

Note 4.   In addition to generating words of a language from an artificial source, as illustrated in Section 2-8, it is possible to generate musical compositions.   Pinkerton (1956) has used this method of musical composition.   Pierce (1961) devotes several pages to the generation of such music; perhaps the ultimate in artistic information theory is displayed in some passages from the "Illiac Suite for String Quartet" reproduced in Pierce (1957, p. 260).

Note 5.   As we have mentioned, the use of the entropy of a source as a measure of the amount of information provided by that source will be justified by Shannon's first theorem (Chapter 4).   It is also possible (Feinstein, 1958) to provide a justification based on the fact that entropy is the only function of the symbol probabilities of a source satisfying certain properties.   Define three zero-memory sources and their symbol probabilities as follows ($\bar{\alpha} = 1 - \alpha$):

S		S_1		S_2	
s_1	P_1	s_1	P_1	s_1	α
s_2	P_2	s_2	P_2	s_2	$\bar{\alpha}$
.	.	.	.		
.	.	.	.		
.	.	.	.		
s_{q-1}	P_{q-1}	s_{q-1}	P_{q-1}		
s_q	P_q	s_q	αP_q		
		s_{q+1}	$\bar{\alpha} P_q$		

Entropy is the unique function (except for a multiplicative constant) of the source symbol probabilities satisfying:
(a) $H(S_1) = H(S) + P_q H(S_2)$.
(b) $H(S_2)$ is a continuous function of α.
(c) $H(S)$ is a symmetric function of $P_1, P_2, \ldots, P_q$.

PROBLEMS

2-1. Prove Equation (2-42).

2-2. The state diagram of a first-order Markov source with source alphabet $S = \{0, 1, 2\}$ is shown in Figure P 2-2.   We define $\bar{p} = 1 - p$.   By symmetry, we see that the stationary distribution is $P(0) = P(1) = P(2) = \frac{1}{3}$.

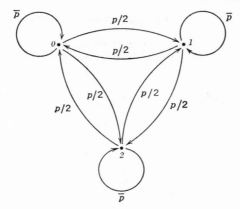

(a) Find $H(\bar{S})$.

(b) Find $H(S)$. Does your answer check for $p = 0$, $p = 1$?

★(c) For which value of p is $H(S)$ a maximum?

(d) Investigate the behavior of $H(S)$ for $p = \epsilon$, where $\epsilon \approx 0$.

(e) Investigate the behavior of $H(S)$ for $p = 1 - \delta$, where $\delta \approx 0$.

(f) Draw the state diagram for S^2.

(g) Find $H(S^2)$, $H(\overline{S^2})$.

2-3. Two zero-memory sources S_1 and S_2 have q_1 and q_2 symbols, respectively. The symbols of S_1 occur with probabilities P_i, $i = 1, 2, \ldots, q_1$; the symbols of S_2 occur with probabilities Q_i, $i = 1, 2, \ldots, q_2$; and the entropies of S_1 and S_2 are H_1 and H_2, respectively. A new zero-memory source $S(\lambda)$, called a *mixture* of S_1 and S_2, is formed with $q_1 + q_2$ symbols. The first q_1 symbols of $S(\lambda)$ have probabilities λP_i, $i = 1, 2, \ldots, q_1$, and the last q_2 symbols of $S(\lambda)$ have probabilities $\bar{\lambda}Q_i$, $i = 1, 2, \ldots, q_2$. ($\bar{\lambda} = 1 - \lambda$.)

(a) Show that

$$H[S(\lambda)] = \lambda H_1 + \bar{\lambda}H_2 + H(\lambda)$$

and provide an interpretation of this equation.

★(b) Express λ_0, the value of λ which maximizes $H[S(\lambda)]$, in terms of H_1 and H_2. Find $H[S(\lambda_0)]$.

2-4. Generalize part a of Problem 2-3 to the case of n zero-memory sources, $S_1, S_2, \ldots, S_n$.

2-5. You may wish to use the identities (for $0 \leq \alpha < 1$)

$$\sum_1^\infty \alpha^n = \frac{\alpha}{1 - \alpha} \qquad \text{and} \qquad \sum_1^\infty n\alpha^n = \frac{\alpha}{(1 - \alpha)^2}$$

in this problem.

(a) A zero-memory information source has a countably infinite symbol alphabet $S = \{s_1, s_2, \ldots\}$ with $P_i = a\alpha^i$ for all i. Express a in terms of α.

(b) Find and sketch $H(S)$ as a function of α. Note particularly the behavior of $H(S)$ for $\alpha \approx 0$ and $\alpha \approx 1$.

2-6. The state diagram of a first-order binary Markov information source is given in Figure P 2-6. The stationary probabilities of this source are $P(0) = q/(p + q)$, $P(1) = p/(p + q)$. You may wish to prove this.

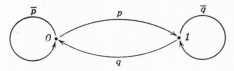

FIGURE P 2-6

   (a) Find $H(S)$.
   (b) Find $H(\bar{S})$.
   (c) Let $q = p$. Find and sketch $H(S)$ as a function of p.
   (d) Find $H(\bar{S})$ when $p = q$.

2-7. (a) Let $q = 1$ for the source of Problem 2-6. (Do not assume $q = p$ here.) Find and sketch $H(S)$ as a function of p.

(b) Still with $q = 1$, find $H(S/0)$ and $H(S/1)$, the information per symbol when the source is in state 0 and 1, respectively.

2-8. (a) Consider a third-order binary Markov source where the probability of emitting a 0 or a 1 does not depend upon the previous two symbols but does depend upon the third symbol back. The probability that the next symbol will be the same as the third symbol back is 0.9: the probability that it will differ is 0.1. Draw the state diagram for this source.

(b) Find the entropy of this source. (The direct method of calculating stationary probabilities, etc., is not the easiest method here.)

2-9. Let S_0 be the third extension of a zero-memory binary source with the probability of a 0 equal to p. Another source S observes the outputs of S_0 and emits either a 0, 1, 2, or 3 according to whether the output of S_0 had 0, 1, 2, or 3 zeros.

   (a) Find $H(S_0)$.
   (b) Find $H(S)$.
   (c) Find $H(S_0) - H(S)$. Provide an interpretation of this entropy difference.

2-10. Generalize part c of Problem 2-9 to the case where S_0 is the nth extension of the binary source and S emits 0, 1, 2, ..., or n. HINT: How much information is lost on the average when we receive a symbol from S rather than from S_0?

2-11. Consider a zero-memory binary information source S_0 with the probability of a 0 equal to $p \approx 1$. Because of the high probability of a run of 0s, one might consider transmitting the lengths of the successive runs of 0s. That is, one can consider a new source S with symbols $s_1, s_2, s_3, \ldots$, where, for instance, the sequence s_3, s_2, s_4, s_1, s_8 would correspond to the binary sequence

$$\underbrace{001}_{s_3}\ \underbrace{01}_{s_2}\ \underbrace{0001}_{s_4}\ \underbrace{1}_{s_1}\ \underbrace{00000001}_{s_8}\ \cdots$$

(a) Find the entropy of S by using the equation

$$H(S) = \sum_S P(s_i) \log \frac{1}{P(s_i)}$$

Do *not* leave your answer in the form of an infinite summation.

(b) Find $H(S)/H(S_0)$.

(c) Find the average number of binits from the original source given by a symbol from S.

2-12. The source S discussed in Problem 2-11 would have to have an infinite number of possible messages s_i. We can consider the source S_n as an approximation to S, where S_n has the $n + 1$ symbols

s_1	1
s_2	01
s_3	001
·	·
·	·
·	·
s_n	0000 · · · 01
s_{n+1}	0000 · · · 00

$$\underbrace{\qquad\qquad}_{n \text{ binits}}$$

(a) Find $H(S_n)$.

(b) Let $p = 0.9$ and sketch $H(S_n)$ as a function of n.

2-13. The state diagram of a first-order Markov source with source alphabet $S = \{0, 1, 2\}$ is shown in Figure P 2-13. By symmetry, the stationary distribution is

$$P(0) = P(1) = P(2) = \tfrac{1}{3}$$

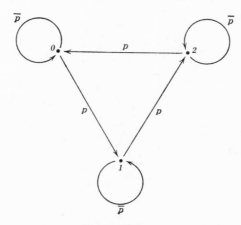

FIGURE P 2-13

(a) Find $H(\bar{S})$.

(b) Find $H(S)$.   Check your answer for $p = 0$, $p = 1$.

(c) Find $H(S^2)$.

2-14. Let S be a zero-memory source with source alphabet $S = \{s_i\}$, $i = 1$, $2, \ldots , q$, and symbol probabilities $P_i, P_2, \ldots , P_q$.   Construct a new zero-memory source S' with twice as many symbols, $S' = \{s_i'\}$, $i = 1, 2, \ldots , 2q$. Let P_i', the symbol probabilities for the new source, be defined by

$$P_i' = (1 - \epsilon)P_i \qquad i = 1, 2, \ldots , q$$
$$P_i' = \epsilon P_{i-q} \qquad i = q + 1, q + 2, \ldots , 2q$$

Express $H(S')$ in terms of $H(S)$.

3

SOME PROPERTIES OF CODES

3-1. Introduction

In order to discuss the connection between coding and the information measure defined in Chapter 2, we shall find it necessary to define certain subclasses of codes. We have already used the general idea of a *code* (Section 1-3) and the related notions of a *code alphabet* and a *source alphabet*.

Definition. Let the set of symbols comprising a given alphabet be called $S = \{s_1, s_2, \ldots, s_q\}$. Then we define a code as a mapping of all possible sequences of symbols of S into sequences of symbols of some other alphabet $X = \{x_1, x_2, \ldots, x_r\}$. We call S the *source alphabet* and X the *code alphabet.*

The definition of a code as given above is too general to be of much use in code synthesis. We therefore restrict our attention to codes having certain additional properties. The first of the properties we require is that the code be a *block code.*

Definition. A *block code* is a code which maps each of the symbols of the source alphabet S into a fixed sequence of symbols of the code alphabet X. These fixed sequences of the code alphabet (sequences of x_j) are called *code words.* We denote the code word corresponding to the source symbol s_i by X_i. Note that X_i denotes a *sequence* of x_j's.†

Example 3-1. An example of a binary block code is given in Table 3-1.

TABLE 3-1. A BINARY BLOCK CODE

Source symbols	Code
s_1	0
s_2	11
s_3	00
s_4	11

At first glance the requirement that we encode the source symbols one at a time into fixed sequences of code symbols seems quite severe. Note, however, that if a code maps all sequences of source symbols of length n into fixed sequences of code symbols, then the code maps each symbol from the nth extension of the original source into a fixed sequence of code symbols, and it is a block code with source alphabet S^n. A set of rules defining a transformation from

† Some authors [e.g., Peterson (1961)] define block codes so that all code words contain the same number of code symbols.

a source alphabet to a code alphabet may satisfy our definition of a block code only when we consider symbols from the nth extension of the source. We shall treat block codes of this type extensively in much of the following material.

3-2. Uniquely Decodable Codes

From the example given above, it is clear that we must put further restrictions on block codes if these codes are to be of use; a natural restriction to put on a code is that all the code words X_i be distinct. Note that X_2 and X_4 of the code given in Table 3-1 are *not* distinct.

> *Definition.* A block code is said to be *nonsingular* if all the words of the code are distinct.

Example 3-2. An example of a nonsingular block code is given in Table 3-2.

TABLE 3-2. A NONSINGULAR BLOCK CODE

Source symbols	Code
s_1	0
s_2	11
s_3	00
s_4	01

Even though all the words are distinct in the example given of a nonsingular block code, it is still possible for a given sequence of code symbols to have an ambiguous origin. For example, the sequence 0011 might represent either $s_3 s_2$ or $s_1 s_1 s_2$. That is, for the code of Table 3-2, even though it is *nonsingular* in the small, it is *singular* in the large. This example shows that we must define an even more restrictive condition than nonsingularity if we are to obtain useful codes.

Let a given block code map symbols from a source alphabet S into fixed sequences of symbols from a code alphabet X. (The source S may be some extension of another source.) Since we restrict ourselves to block codes, we have a natural elementary code unit—namely, the symbol from S and its corresponding word composed of letters from the code alphabet. We may put these building blocks together, just as we put successive symbols from an elementary source together to form an extension of a source.

Definition. The nth extension of a block code which maps the symbols s_i into the code words X_i is the block code which maps the sequences of source symbols $(s_{i_1} s_{i_2} \cdots s_{i_n})$ into the sequences of code words $(X_{i_1} X_{i_2} \cdots X_{i_n})$.

From the above definition, we see that the nth extension of a block code is also a block code.

Example 3-3. The second extension of the block code of Table 3-2 is shown in Table 3-3.

TABLE 3-3. THE SECOND EXTENSION OF A BLOCK CODE

Source symbols	Code	Source symbols	Code
$s_1 s_1$	00	$s_3 s_1$	000
$s_1 s_2$	011	$s_3 s_2$	0011
$s_1 s_3$	000	$s_3 s_3$	0000
$s_1 s_4$	001	$s_3 s_4$	0001
$s_2 s_1$	110	$s_4 s_1$	010
$s_2 s_2$	1111	$s_4 s_2$	0111
$s_2 s_3$	1100	$s_4 s_3$	0100
$s_2 s_4$	1101	$s_4 s_4$	0101

Definition. A block code is said to be *uniquely decodable* if, and only if, the nth extension of the code is nonsingular for every finite n.

Our definition assures us that any two sequences of source symbols *of the same length* lead to distinct sequences of code symbols. Clearly, we should also require any two sequences of source symbols, even if they are not of the same length, to lead to distinct sequences of code symbols. This property follows easily from our definition. Let us, for instance, assume the contrary. That is, we assume that there are two sequences, S_1 and S_2, of source symbols which lead to the same sequence of code symbols, X_0. Note that S_1, S_2, and X_0 represent *sequences* of symbols and not merely single symbols. Furthermore, S_1 and S_2 may be sequences of source symbols of different lengths. Now let us form two new sequences of source symbols, S_1' and S_2'. S_1' is defined as that sequence of source symbols consisting of S_2 followed by S_1. S_2' is defined as that sequence of source symbols consisting of S_1 followed by S_2. We see that both S_1' and S_2' lead to a sequence of code symbols which is merely X_0 followed by X_0. Both S_1' and S_2' are also of the same length. Thus, the code does not satisfy the condition of unique decodability given above.

Sardinas and Patterson (1953) have found necessary and sufficient conditions for unique decodability. Since we shall be concerned with a subclass of uniquely decodable codes, we do not need their result here.

3-3. Instantaneous Codes

Two examples of uniquely decodable codes are given in Table 3-4.†

TABLE 3-4. TWO UNIQUELY DECODABLE CODES

Source symbols	Code $\mathcal{A}$	Code $\mathcal{B}$
s_1	00	0
s_2	01	10
s_3	10	110
s_4	11	1110

Code $\mathcal{A}$ given above illustrates what is undoubtedly the simplest method of constructing a uniquely decodable code. All the words of $\mathcal{A}$ are of the same length, and, in addition, $\mathcal{A}$ is obviously non-singular. It can be seen that these two properties are sufficient to ensure unique decodability.

Code $\mathcal{B}$ in Table 3-4 is uniquely decodable because it is non-singular, and, in addition, it is what has been called a *comma code*. That is, in $\mathcal{B}$ the 0 acts as a comma to separate one word from the next. When scanning a sequence of code symbols, we may use the comma to determine when one word ends and another begins.

The ability to tell when a code word, immersed in a finite sequence

† From now on we shall use script letters to denote codes.

of code symbols, comes to an end can be seen to be central to the construction of both types of uniquely decodable codes discussed above.   Indeed this property is at the very heart of the uniquely decodable concept.   Consider yet another uniquely decodable code (Table 3-5).

TABLE 3-5. ANOTHER UNIQUELY DECODABLE CODE

Source symbols	Code $\mathfrak{C}$
s_1	0
s_2	01
s_3	011
s_4	0111

Code $\mathfrak{C}$ is different from codes $\mathfrak{A}$ and $\mathfrak{B}$ of Table 3-4 in an important respect.   If we are given a binary sequence composed of words from code $\mathfrak{C}$, we are not able to decode the sequence, word by word, *as it is received*.   If we receive 01, for example, we cannot say that this corresponds to the source symbol s_2 until we receive the next code symbol.   If the next code symbol is 0, then we know the 01 corresponded to s_2; if, however, the next code symbol is 1, then we would have to inspect one more code symbol to tell us whether we were receiving s_3(011) or s_4(0111).   This time lag is essential to the decoding process if we use code $\mathfrak{C}$, whereas with code $\mathfrak{A}$ or $\mathfrak{B}$ we are able to decode each word as it arrives.

Definition.   A uniquely decodable code is said to be *instantaneous* if it is possible to decode each word in a sequence without reference to succeeding code symbols.

Codes $\mathfrak{A}$ and $\mathfrak{B}$ given above are instantaneous.   Code $\mathfrak{C}$ is an example of a uniquely decodable code which is *not* instantaneous. In these three cases it is easy to test the code to see whether it is instantaneous.   It will be useful to have a general test for a code which will tell us when a code is instantaneous; we now develop such a test.

Definition.   Let $X_i = x_{i_1} x_{i_2} \cdots x_{i_m}$ be a word of some code.   The sequence of code symbols $(x_{i_1} x_{i_2} \cdots x_{i_j})$, where $j \leq m$, is called a *prefix* of the code word X_i.

Example 3-4. The code word 0111 has four prefixes—0111, 011, 01, and 0.

The test we seek may now be stated:

> A necessary and sufficient condition for a code
> to be instantaneous is that no complete word
> of the code be a prefix of some other code word.   (3-1)

The *sufficient* part of the test given above follows directly from our definition of instantaneous. If no word is the prefix of some other word, we may decode any received sequence of code symbols comprised of code words in a direct manner. We scan the received sequence of code symbols until we come to a subsequence which comprises a complete code word. The subsequence must be this code word since by assumption it is not the prefix of any other code word. In this manner we may proceed decoding words one by one, without any time lag in the decoding process.

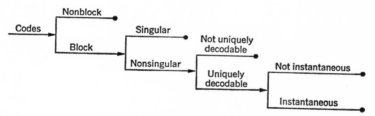

FIGURE 3-1. Subclasses of codes.

The *necessary* part of the test may be demonstrated by assuming the contrary and deriving a contradiction. We assume that there exists some word of our code, say X_i, which is also a prefix of some other word X_j. Now, if we scan a received sequence of code symbols and come upon the subsequence X_i, this subsequence may be a complete word, or it may be just the first part of word X_j. We cannot possibly tell which of these alternatives is true, however, until we examine more code symbols of the main sequence—thus the code is not instantaneous.

At this point it is helpful to summarize the various classes of codes we have dealt with in the preceding pages. In Figure 3-1 we indicate the path defined through our maze of subclasses of codes which finally led us to the subclass of instantaneous codes.

3-4. Construction of an Instantaneous Code

The nature of the constraints imposed upon a code when we require it to be instantaneous may be appreciated more fully by some primitive attempts at code synthesis. Let us try to synthesize a binary instantaneous code for a source with five symbols. We might start by assigning 0 to symbol s_1:

$$s_1 \rightarrow 0$$

If this is the case, then note that all other source symbols *must* correspond to code words beginning with 1. If this were not true, we would contradict rule (3-1). We cannot let s_2 correspond to the single symbol code word 1; this would leave us with no symbols with which to start the remaining three code words. We might have

$$s_2 \rightarrow 10$$

This, in turn, would require us to start the remaining code words with 11. If

$$s_3 \rightarrow 110$$

then the only three-binit prefix still unused is 111 and we might set

$$s_4 \rightarrow 1110$$

and

$$s_5 \rightarrow 1111$$

In the above code, note how starting the code by letting s_1 correspond to 0 cut down the number of possible code words. Once we had taken this step we were restricted to code words starting with 1. We might expect, therefore, that if we were to select a 2-binit code word to represent s_1, we would have more freedom of selection in the ensuing words, and we might not have to use two code words as long as the last two words in the code just constructed. To test this conjecture, we synthesize another binary instantaneous code for our five symbols; this time we start by setting

$$s_1 \rightarrow 00$$

Then we may set

$$s_2 \rightarrow 01$$

and we still have two prefixes of length 2 which are unused. We may use these as shown on the next page.

$$s_3 \rightarrow 10$$
$$s_4 \rightarrow 110$$
$$s_5 \rightarrow 111$$

The question of which of the two codes constructed above is better cannot be resolved on the basis of the information given. Our two coding examples show that in the construction of an instantaneous code, the shorter we make the first few words of the code, the longer we will have to make the later words.   By using 0 as a word in the first code, we restricted all later words to sequences starting with 1.   In the second code, we used 00 as the first word. In this case, we were able to form later words by starting with 1 and in addition we could use words starting with 01.

3-5. The Kraft Inequality—Statement and Discussion

In Section 3-4 we discussed qualitatively certain constraints on the size of words of an instantaneous code.   It is also possible to express the constraints illustrated in a quantitative fashion.   The rest of this chapter will be concerned with quantitative constraints on the word lengths of a code.

Consider an instantaneous code with source alphabet

$$S = \{s_1, s_2, \ldots, s_q\}$$

and code alphabet $X = \{x_1, x_2, \ldots, x_r\}$.   Let the code words be $X_1, X_2, \ldots, X_q$ and define the length (i.e., number of code symbols) of word X_i as l_i.   It is often desirable that the lengths of the code words of our code be as small as possible.   Necessary and sufficient conditions for the existence of an instantaneous code with word lengths $l_1, l_2, \ldots, l_q$ are provided by the *Kraft inequality* (Kraft, 1949).

A necessary and sufficient condition for the existence of an instantaneous code with word lengths $l_1, l_2, \ldots, l_q$ is that

number of words = number of source symbols

$$\sum_{i=1}^{q} r^{-l_i} \leq 1$$

where r is the number of different symbols in the code alphabet.

(3-2)

For the binary case, the Kraft inequality tells us that the l_i must satisfy the equation

$$\sum_{i=1}^{q} 2^{-l_i} \leq 1 \qquad (3\text{-}3)$$

where the summation is over all the words of the block code. Before proving the Kraft inequality, it will be instructive to show how one might use the inequality to determine whether a given sequence of l_i is acceptable as the lengths of the code words for an instantaneous code.

Let us take an information source with four possible symbols, s_1, s_2, s_3, and s_4. In Table 3-6 we have listed five possible codes for encoding the symbols of this source into a binary alphabet.

TABLE 3-6. FIVE BINARY CODES

Source symbols	Code α	Code $\mathcal{B}$	Code $\mathcal{C}$	Code $\mathcal{D}$	Code $\mathcal{E}$
s_1	00	0	0	0	0
s_2	01	100	10	100	10
s_3	10	110	110	110	110
s_4	11	111	111	11	11

Now we calculate $\sum_{i=1}^{4} 2^{-l_i}$ for each of these codes.

For code α we see that

$$\sum_{i=1}^{4} 2^{-l_i} = 2^{-2} + 2^{-2} + 2^{-2} + 2^{-2}$$
$$= 1$$

Hence, the word lengths of code α are acceptable as the word lengths of an instantaneous code. Note, however, that the Kraft inequality does *not* tell us that code α is an instantaneous code. The inequality is merely a condition on the word *lengths* of the code and *not* on the words themselves. In particular, for this example the Kraft inequality says that there does exist an instantaneous binary code with four code words, each of length 2. In this case it is clear not only that the word lengths of code $\mathcal{C}$ satisfy the Kraft inequality, but also that the words themselves do comprise an instantaneous code.

For code $\mathcal{B}$ we calculate

$$\sum_{i=1}^{4} 2^{-l_i} = 2^{-1} + 2^{-3} + 2^{-3} + 2^{-3}$$
$$= \tfrac{7}{8}$$
$$\leq 1$$

Again, we see that the word lengths of this code are acceptable as word lengths of an instantaneous code.   Furthermore, from inspection of the code words themselves, we see that code $\mathcal{B}$ satisfies condition (3-1) and is, therefore, actually instantaneous.   Code $\mathcal{C}$ is identical with code $\mathcal{B}$ except that we have dropped one binit from the second code word.   We calculate

$$\sum_{i=1}^{4} 2^{-l_i} = 2^{-1} + 2^{-2} + 2^{-3} + 2^{-3}$$
$$= 1$$

and this set of word lengths again satisfies the Kraft inequality. In addition, upon checking, we again find that code $\mathcal{C}$ is instantaneous.   Code $\mathcal{D}$ is also obtained from code $\mathcal{B}$ by dropping one binit (this time from the fourth word).   We find that the word lengths of code $\mathcal{D}$ satisfy the Kraft inequality.   As we have mentioned, this does not ensure that code $\mathcal{D}$ is instantaneous, and indeed we see that the fourth code word is a prefix of the third code word. Condition (3-1) is thus violated, and code $\mathcal{D}$ is *not* instantaneous.

Finally, for code $\mathcal{E}$ of Table 3-6, we calculate

$$\sum_{i=1}^{4} 2^{-l_i} = 2^{-1} + 2^{-2} + 2^{-3} + 2^{-2}$$
$$= 1\tfrac{1}{8}$$

For this code no further investigation is required.   The word lengths do not satisfy the Kraft inequality, and therefore code $\mathcal{E}$ could not possibly be an instantaneous block code.

We consider one more example before proceeding to the proof of the Kraft inequality.   Suppose we wish to encode the outputs of a decimal source, $S = \{0, 1, 2, \ldots, 9\}$, into a binary instantaneous code.   Further, let us suppose there is some reason for encoding the 0 and the 1 symbols of the decimal source into relatively short binary code words.   This is a realistic requirement for a source which emits many more 0s and 1s than 2s, 3s, etc.   If we were to encode 0s and 1s from the source as†

$$0 \rightarrow 0$$
$$1 \rightarrow 10$$

(3-4)

then we might be interested in the question of how short it is possible to make the remaining eight code words.   If we require all these eight code words to be of the same length, say l, the Kraft

TABLE 3-7. A BINARY CODE FOR DECIMAL DIGITS

Decimal digits	Binary code
0	0
1	10
2	11000
3	11001
4	11010
5	11011
6	11100
7	11101
8	11110
9	11111

inequality will provide us with a direct answer to the question.   By the inequality we know we must have

$$\sum_{i=0}^{9} 2^{-l_i} \leq 1$$

(3-5)

By assumption we have $l_0 = 1$, $l_1 = 2$, and $l_2 = l_3 = \cdots = l_9 = l$.   Putting these relations in (3-5), we find

$$\tfrac{1}{2} + \tfrac{1}{4} + 8(2^{-l}) \leq 1$$

or

$$l \geq 5$$

(3-6)

† We could not encode $0 \rightarrow 0$ and $1 \rightarrow 1$ since this would exhaust all possible single-binit prefixes before we had encoded the remaining eight source symbols, and we would not be able to construct an instantaneous code.

It is not possible, therefore, to find an instantaneous code meeting our requirements when $l < 5$. The Kraft inequality tells us that such a code exists with l equal to 5, but it does not tell us how to construct this code. The code we seek, however, is not hard to find; it is given in Table 3-7.

3-6. The Kraft Inequality—Proof

In the previous section we presented the Kraft inequality, together with some examples designed to help the reader obtain an understanding of the nature of the constraints imposed by this inequality. Now we organize and rearrange these constraints into a proof of the inequality. First, we prove that the inequality is sufficient for the existence of an instantaneous code by actually constructing an instantaneous code satisfying

$$\sum_{i=1}^{q} r^{-l_i} \leq 1 \tag{3-7}$$

Assume that we are given word lengths $l_1, l_2, \ldots, l_q$ satisfying (3-7), and that we are required to construct an instantaneous code with these word lengths. The required word lengths, $l_1, l_2, \ldots, l_q$, may or may not be all distinct. We shall find it useful in our construction to consider all words of the same length at one time. Let us, therefore, define n_1 to be the number of words in our code of length 1; n_2 to be the number of words of length 2; etc. If the largest of the l_i is equal to l, we have

$$\sum_{i=1}^{l} n_i = q \tag{3-8}$$

restriction on $l = i_{max}$

We may use the n_i to rewrite (3-7). The summation of (3-7) contains n_1 terms of the form r^{-1}, n_2 terms of the form r^{-2}, etc. It may then be written as

$$\sum_{i=1}^{l} n_i r^{-i} \leq 1 \tag{3-9}$$

or, on multiplying by r^l,

$$\sum_{i=1}^{l} n_i r^{l-i} \leq r^l \tag{3-10}$$

Upon writing out this equation and rearranging terms, we get

$$n_l \leq r^l - n_1 r^{l-1} - n_2 r^{l-2} - \cdots - n_{l-1} r \qquad (3\text{-}11a)$$

We may obtain an interesting sequence of inequalities from (3-11a) by dropping the term on the left and dividing by r.

$$n_{l-1} \leq r^{l-1} - n_1 r^{l-2} - n_2 r^{l-3} - \cdots - n_{l-2} r \qquad (3\text{-}11b)$$
$$\cdots\cdots\cdots\cdots\cdots\cdots\cdots\cdots\cdots\cdots$$
$$n_3 \leq r^3 - n_1 r^2 - n_2 r \qquad (3\text{-}11c)$$
$$n_2 \leq r^2 - n_1 r \qquad (3\text{-}11d)$$
$$n_1 \leq r \qquad (3\text{-}11e)$$

Total number of words = q ≤ $n_i = q$

This set of inequalities is the key to the construction of the code we seek. We are required to form n_1 words of length 1. There are r possible such words that we may form, using an r-symbol code alphabet. Since $n_1 \leq r$, we can select these n_1 code symbols arbitrarily. Let us do so; we are then left with $r - n_1$ permissible prefixes of length 1—namely, just those prefixes which were not used as code words. By adding one symbol to the end of each of these permissible prefixes, we may form as many as

$$(r - n_1)r = r^2 - n_1 r \qquad (3\text{-}12)$$

words of length 2. Equation (3-11d), however, assures us that we shall need no more than this number of words of length 2. As before, we choose our n_2 words arbitrarily from among our $r^2 - n_1 r$ choices; we are then left with

$$(r^2 - n_1 r) - n_2$$

unused prefixes of length 2, from which we may form

$$(r^2 - n_1 r - n_2)r = r^3 - n_1 r^2 - n_2 r \qquad (3\text{-}13)$$

permissible prefixes of length 3. Again we are assured that we shall need no more than this number (3-11c), and we select our words of length 3 arbitrarily from among these. We may proceed in this fashion until we have formed all the words of our code. Equations (3-11) assure us at each stage that we have enough prefixes left. *unused*

Having demonstrated that (3-7) [or equivalently (3-9)] is sufficient *form* for the construction of an instantaneous code with word lengths *the* $l_1, l_2, \ldots l_q$, it is a relatively simple matter to show that this equation is also a necessary condition. We need only reverse the arguments we have already used. Instead of carrying out this procedure in detail, we shall prove a much stronger result.

3-7. McMillan's Inequality

In the previous section we proved that

$$\sum_{i=1}^{q} r^{-l_i} \leq 1 \tag{3-14}$$

provides a sufficient condition on the word lengths of an *instantaneous* code by showing how to construct such a code with the prescribed word lengths. Since instantaneous codes form a subclass of *uniquely decodable* codes, the *sufficient* part of our results also applies to uniquely decodable codes; that is, we can construct a *uniquely decodable* code with word lengths $l_1, l_2, \ldots, l_q$ if these lengths satisfy (3-14).

A proof of the necessity of the Kraft inequality, on the other hand, cannot be applied to uniquely decodable codes. In fact, the *necessary* part of the Kraft inequality suggests an investigation of the constraints on the word lengths of uniquely decodable codes. We know that (3-14) expresses a necessary condition for instantaneous codes. Does the same condition hold for the more general uniquely decodable codes?

The fact that (3-14) is necessary for uniquely decodable codes, as well as instantaneous codes, was first proved by McMillan (1956). McMillan's proof was subsequently simplified by Karush (1961). Consider the quantity

$$\Big(\sum_{i=1}^{q} r^{-l_i}\Big)^n = (r^{-l_1} + r^{-l_2} + \cdots + r^{-l_q})^n \tag{3-15}$$

when multiplied out w/o adding identical terms

When written out, (3-15) will have q^n terms, each of the form

$$r^{-l_{i_1}-l_{i_2}-\cdots-l_{i_n}} = r^{-k} \tag{3-16}$$

where we have defined

$$l_{i_1} + l_{i_2} + \cdots + l_{i_n} = k \tag{3-17}$$

As in the previous section, we let l be the maximum of the word lengths l_i. Then k can assume some set of values from n to nl. We define N_k as the number of terms of the form r^{-k} in (3-15). Then

$$\left(\sum_{i=1}^{q} r^{-l_i} \right)^n = \sum_{k=n}^{nl} N_k r^{-k} \tag{3-18}$$

But from (3-17) we see that N_k is also the number of strings of n code words that can be formed so that each string has a length of exactly k code symbols. If the code is uniquely decodable, N_k must be no greater than r^k, the number of distinct r-ary sequences of length k. Thus

$$\left(\sum_{i=1}^{q} r^{-l_i} \right)^n \leq \sum_{k=n}^{nl} r^k r^{-k}$$

$$\leq nl - n + 1$$
$$\leq nl \tag{3-19}$$

Equation (3-19) is the proof we seek, for if $x > 1$, then $x^n > nl$ if we take n large enough. Equation (3-19) holds for any integer n; so we must have

$$\sum_{i=1}^{q} r^{-l_i} \leq 1 \tag{3-20}$$

3-8. Some Examples

We end this chapter dealing with the properties of codes with two more illustrations of the Kraft inequality and an example of the construction of an instantaneous code.

First, assume we wish to encode a source with 10 source symbols into a trinary instantaneous code with word lengths 1, 2, 2, 2, 2, 2, 3, 3, 3, 3. Applying the test of the Kraft inequality, we calculate

$$\sum_{i=1}^{10} 3^{-l_i} = \tfrac{1}{3} + 5(\tfrac{1}{9}) + 4(\tfrac{1}{27})$$

$$= \tfrac{28}{27} > 1$$

It is not possible, therefore, to find an instantaneous trinary code with these word lengths.

For the second example, assume that we wish to encode symbols from a source with nine symbols into a trinary instantaneous code with word lengths 1, 2, 2, 2, 2, 2, 3, 3, 3.   This time, upon applying our test, we find

$$\sum_{i=1}^{9} 3^{-l_i} = \tfrac{1}{3} + 5(\tfrac{1}{9}) + 3(\tfrac{1}{27})$$

$$= 1$$

Therefore, the code we seek is possible.   It is given as follows:

$$s_1 \rightarrow 0$$
$$s_2 \rightarrow 10$$
$$s_3 \rightarrow 11$$
$$s_4 \rightarrow 12$$
$$s_5 \rightarrow 20$$
$$s_6 \rightarrow 21$$
$$s_7 \rightarrow 220$$
$$s_8 \rightarrow 221$$
$$s_9 \rightarrow 222$$

Note how the construction of the above code illustrates the coding method used in the proof of the Kraft inequality.   We used one prefix of length 1 (namely, 0), and we were then restricted to the remaining two prefixes of length 1 for the other code words.   This left us with two times three, or six, permissible code words of length 2.   We used only five of these possibilites, saving the sixth (22) for use as a prefix in the three final words.

NOTES

Note 1.   A method of constructing a nonblock code which is uniquely decodable in the colloquial sense (but not in the sense defined in Section 3-2) is due to Elias.   To illustrate his method, consider a zero-memory source with two symbols A and B, occurring with probability 0.7 and 0.3, respectively.   We may

represent an arbitrary infinite-output sequence from such a source as a point in the interval [0, 1] as indicated above.   (Sequences starting with A are assigned to the interval [0, 0.7]; sequences starting with AB are assigned to the interval [0.49, 0.70]; etc.)   To encode a sequence from this source we merely provide a binary expansion for each point in [0, 1] as follows:

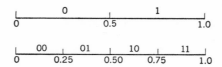

Note that it is *not* necessary to receive the complete binary sequence before we start decoding.   For example, if the binary sequence starts with $011 \cdot \cdot \cdot$, we know that the point represented must lie between 0.375 and 0.50; hence the first symbol from the source must be A.   If the binary sequence starts with 0110, the point represented must lie between 0.375 and 0.4375; hence the first three symbols from the source must be AAB.

This idea is the basis of a novel proof of Shannon's first theorem (Section 4-3; Chapter 4, Note 1) due to Billingsley (1961).   Billingsley expresses sequences from an information source as a point in the unit interval and uses results from the theory of Hausdorff dimension to show that the natural r-adic expansion provides the most efficient specification of this point.

Note 2.   One of the most interesting applications of the ideas discussed in Chapter 3 is that of genetic coding (Golomb, 1961, 1962).   It has been determined that the vast amount of information necessary to specify the structure of a biological system is contained in the chromosomes of the parent system. More precisely it is the deoxyribonucleic acid (DNA) contained in the chromosomes which transmits the genetic information.   In 1953 Crick and Watson showed that DNA existed in the form of a double helix.   These helices may be thought of as being connected by sequences of four nucleotides which comprise the genetic message.   The nucleotides, usually designated A, C, G, and T (for adenine, cytosine, guanine, and thymine), correspond to the code symbols discussed in Chapter 3.   Experimental evidence therefore indicates that nature operates with a four-symbol code alphabet.   These code symbols are combined in some manner to represent about twenty amino acids which must be manufactured by the new biological system.   The manner in which nucleotides (A, C, G, T) are coded to represent the different amino acids is the primary problem in genetic coding.

PROBLEMS

3-1. An instantaneous code has word lengths l_1, l_2, . . . , l_q which satisfy the strict inequality

$$\sum_{i=1}^{q} r^{-l_i} < 1$$

The code alphabet is $X = \{x_1, x_2, \ldots , x_r\}$.   Show that there exist sequences of code symbols $x_{i_1}, x_{i_2}, x_{i_3}, \ldots$ which cannot be decoded into sequences of code words.

3-2. A source has six possible outputs with probabilities as shown in Table P 3-2. Codes α, $\mathfrak{B}$, $\mathfrak{C}$, $\mathfrak{D}$, $\mathcal{E}$, and $\mathfrak{F}$, as given in the table, are considered.

(a) Which of these codes are uniquely decodable?

(b) Which are instantaneous?

(c) Find the average length L for all the uniquely decodable codes.

TABLE P 3-2

Output	$P(s_i)$	α	$\mathfrak{B}$	$\mathfrak{C}$	$\mathfrak{D}$	$\mathcal{E}$	$\mathfrak{F}$
s_1	$\frac{1}{2}$	000	0	0	0	0	0
s_2	$\frac{1}{4}$	001	01	10	10	10	100
s_3	$\frac{1}{16}$	010	011	110	110	1100	101
s_4	$\frac{1}{16}$	011	0111	1110	1110	1101	110
s_5	$\frac{1}{16}$	100	01111	11110	1011	1110	111
s_6	$\frac{1}{16}$	101	011111	111110	1101	1111	001

3-3. (a) Which of the sets of word lengths shown in Table P 3-3 are acceptable for a uniquely decodable code when the code alphabet is $X = \{0, 1, 2\}$?

TABLE P 3-3

	Word length l_i				
	1	2	3	4	5
Number of words of length l_i in each code:					
Code α	2	1	2	4	1
Code $\mathfrak{B}$	2	2	2	3	1
Code $\mathfrak{C}$	1	4	6	0	0
Code $\mathfrak{D}$	2	2	2	2	3

(b) Construct an instantaneous code for each set of acceptable lengths in the table.

3-4. A zero-memory source has the alphabet $S = \{a, b, c\}$ with probabilities 0.6, 0.3, and 0.1, respectively. This source is encoded into a nonblock binary code using the method described above in Note 1. Find as many of the first binits of the code word corresponding to $acbcaab \cdots$ as possible.

4

CODING
INFORMATION
SOURCES

4-1. The Average Length of a Code

In Chapter 3 we have shown how to construct instantaneous codes which map symbols from a source alphabet into words composed of symbols from some code alphabet. For a given source alphabet and a given code alphabet, however, we can construct many instantaneous or uniquely decodable codes. This abundance of acceptable codes forces us to find a criterion by which we may choose among the codes. Perhaps the natural criterion for this selection, although by no means the only possibility, is length.

We have, in fact, already used this criterion explicitly in the examples of Chapter 1, and implicitly in several of our later coding discussions.

If there are no other considerations, from the standpoint of mere economy of expression and the resulting economy of communication equipment, we prefer a code with many short words to one with long words. We therefore define the average length of a code.

Definition. Let a block code transform the source symbols $s_1, s_2, \ldots, s_q$ into the code words $X_1, X_2, \ldots, X_q$. Let the probabilities of the source symbols be $P_1, P_2, \ldots, P_q$, and let the lengths of the code words be $l_1, l_2, \ldots, l_q$. Then we define L, the *average length* of the code, by the equation

$$ L = \sum_{i=1}^{q} P_i l_i \qquad (4\text{-}1) $$

We shall be interested in finding uniquely decodable codes with average length as small as possible.

Definition. Consider a uniquely decodable code which maps the symbols from a source S into code words composed of symbols from an r-ary code alphabet. This code will be called *compact* (for the source S) if its average length is less than or equal to the average length of all other uniquely decodable codes for the same source and the same code alphabet.

Using these two definitions, we may formulate the fundamental problem of coding information sources as that of finding compact codes. Note that both definitions refer only to the word *lengths* of codes, and not to the words themselves. Because of this, we may restrict our search for compact codes to the class of instantaneous codes (Section 3-7). McMillan's inequality assures us that any set of word lengths achievable in a uniquely decodable code is also achievable in an instantaneous code. As the first step in our search, we find the minimum value of L that it is possible to achieve with an instantaneous code.

Our definition of L is valid for either zero-memory or Markov information sources. In order to simplify the discussion, however, we temporarily limit our considerations to zero-memory sources. In Section 4-4 we remove this restriction.

Consider a zero-memory source S, with symbols $s_1, s_2, \ldots, s_q$ and symbol probabilities $P_1, P_2, \ldots, P_q$, respectively. Let a block code encode these symbols into a code alphabet of r symbols, and let the length of the word corresponding to s_i be l_i. Then the entropy of this zero-memory source is

$$H(S) = - \sum_{i=1}^{q} P_i \log P_i \tag{4-2}$$

Let $Q_1, Q_2, \ldots, Q_q$ be any q numbers such that $Q_i \geq 0$ for all i and $\sum_{i=1}^{q} Q_i = 1$. By the inequality (2-8), we know that

$$\sum_{i=1}^{q} P_i \log \frac{1}{P_i} \leq \sum_{i=1}^{q} P_i \log \frac{1}{Q_i} \tag{4-3}$$

with equality if and only if $P_i = Q_i$ for all i. Hence

$$H(S) \leq - \sum_{i=1}^{q} P_i \log Q_i \tag{4-4}$$

with equality if and only if $P_i = Q_i$ for all i.

Equation (4-4) is valid for any set of nonnegative numbers Q_i which sum to 1. We may, therefore, choose

$$Q_i = \frac{r^{-l_i}}{\sum_{i=1}^{q} r^{-l_i}} \tag{4-5}$$

and obtain

$$H(S) \leq - \sum_{i=1}^{q} P_i(\log r^{-l_i}) + \sum_{i=1}^{q} P_i \left(\log \sum_{j=1}^{q} r^{-l_i} \right)$$
$$\leq \log r \sum_{i=1}^{q} P_i l_i + \log \left(\sum_{j=1}^{q} r^{-l_i} \right)$$
$$\leq L \log r + \log \sum_{j=1}^{q} r^{-l_i} \tag{4-6}$$

If we add the requirement that our code be instantaneous, the Kraft inequality tells us that the argument of the second logarithm on the right of (4-6) must be less than or equal to 1. The logarithm is, therefore, less than or equal to 0, and

$$H(S) \leq L \log r \quad \text{(4-7a)}$$

is a stronger (4-7a) inequality dumping zero or less

or

$$\frac{H(S)}{\log r} \leq L \quad \text{(4-7b)}$$

$H(S)$ in (4-7b) is measured in bits. Recall that L is the average number of r-ary symbols we use to encode S. If we measure the entropy in r-ary units also, as in (2-5c), then (4-7b) may be written

$$H_r(S) \leq L \quad \text{(4-7c)}$$

4-2. A Method of Encoding for Special Sources

It should be noted that (4-7) constitutes a milestone in our study of information theory. This equation is the first instance which demonstrates the connection between our definition of information and a quantity (in this case L) *which does not depend upon that definition*. With this equation we have started to present the justification for our information measure.

On the surface, (4-7) merely presents us with a bound on L, the average length of an instantaneous code. In certain cases, however, it is possible to show much more from the simple arguments leading to that equation. We do this by carefully examining the conditions for equality in (4-7). The inequality of (4-7) was introduced at two points—first at (4-4), and then when we dropped the second term of (4-6). From (4-6) we see that a necessary condition for the equality rather than inequality of (4-7) is

because then the most is taken away from the larger side of the inequality, namely zero

$$\sum_{j=1}^{q} r^{-l_j} = 1 \quad \text{(4-8)}$$

Then, retracing our steps to (4-4), we see that a necessary and sufficient condition for equality is

$$P_i = Q_i$$
$$= \frac{r^{-l_i}}{\sum_{j=1}^{q} r^{-l_j}} \longrightarrow = 1$$
$$= r^{-l_i} \quad \text{for all } i \quad \text{(4-9a)}$$

if $P_i = r^{-l_i}$ then L is as sho... it can not... ... equal to H(s)... lower

inverting and

or   *taking the log of both sides*

$$\log_r \frac{1}{P_i} = l_i \qquad \text{for all } i \qquad (4\text{-}9b)$$

Summing up the preceding material, we may say that, for an instantaneous code and a zero-memory source, L must be greater than or equal to $H_r(S)$. Furthermore, L can achieve this lower bound *if and only if* we can choose the word lengths l_i equal to $\log_r (1/P_i)$ for all i. For the equality, therefore, $\log_r (1/P_i)$ must be an *integer* for each i.

Put another way, we see that for equality the symbol probabilities P_i must all be of the form $(1/r)^{\alpha_i}$, where α_i is an integer. As an additional windfall, we note that *if these conditions are met, we have derived the word lengths of a compact code*. We simply choose l_i equal to α_i. Having obtained the word lengths, the construction of a compact code follows the procedure of Section 3-8.

Example 4-1.   We have reached the point where we can answer some of the coding questions raised in Chapter 1. In Table 4-1 we reproduce a zero-memory source first defined in Table 1-4.

TABLE 4-1. AN INFORMATION SOURCE

Source symbol	Symbol probability P_i
s_1	$\frac{1}{4}$
s_2	$\frac{1}{4}$
s_3	$\frac{1}{4}$
s_4	$\frac{1}{4}$

We calculate the entropy of this source:

$$H = \sum_{i=1}^{4} P_i \log \frac{1}{P_i}$$
$$= 2 \text{ bits/symbol}$$

From (4-7c) we know that it is *impossible* to encode the symbols from this source into a uniquely decodable binary code with average length L less than 2 binits per symbol. Each symbol of the source has a probability of $\frac{1}{4} = (\frac{1}{2})^2$, and so [(4-9b)] a compact code must have four words of length 2. Such a code was given in Chapter 1. It is

$$s_1 \rightarrow 00$$
$$s_2 \rightarrow 01$$
$$s_3 \rightarrow 10$$
$$s_4 \rightarrow 11$$

The average word length of this code is 2 binits per symbol, and there exists no uniquely decodable code for this source with smaller average word length.

In Table 1-5, we defined another zero-memory source as shown in Table 4-2.

TABLE 4-2. AN INFORMATION SOURCE

Source symbol	Symbol probability P_i
s_1	$\frac{1}{2}$
s_2	$\frac{1}{4}$
s_3	$\frac{1}{8}$
s_4	$\frac{1}{8}$

The entropy of this source is

$$H = \sum_{i=1}^{4} P_i \log \frac{1}{P_i}$$
$$= \tfrac{1}{2} \log 2 + \tfrac{1}{4} \log 4 + \tfrac{1}{8} \log 8 + \tfrac{1}{8} \log 8$$
$$= 1\tfrac{3}{4} \text{ bits/symbol}$$

The smallest possible average length we are able to achieve in a binary instantaneous code for this source is, therefore, $1\tfrac{3}{4}$ binits per symbol. In Chapter 1 the best we were able to find used an average of $1\tfrac{7}{8}$ binits per symbol. All the symbol probabilities of this source are of the form $(\tfrac{1}{2})^{\alpha_i}$, with α_i integer, however, and so it is possible to achieve the lower bound of $1\tfrac{3}{4}$ binits per symbol. From (4-9b) we see this is done by setting the word lengths equal to 1, 2, 3, and 3, respectively. The code is

$$s_1 \rightarrow 0$$
$$s_2 \rightarrow 10$$
$$s_3 \rightarrow 110$$
$$s_4 \rightarrow 111$$

As a check, we calculate L directly:

$$L = \sum_{i=1}^{4} P_i l_i = 1\tfrac{3}{4} \text{ binits/symbol}$$

Example 4-2. As a final illustration of coding when the bound given in Equations (4-7) can be achieved, consider the zero-memory source with seven symbols shown in Table 4-3.

TABLE 4-3. AN INFORMATION SOURCE

Source symbol	Symbol probability P_i
s_1	$\frac{1}{3}$
s_2	$\frac{1}{3}$
s_3	$\frac{1}{9}$
s_4	$\frac{1}{9}$
s_5	$\frac{1}{27}$
s_6	$\frac{1}{27}$
s_7	$\frac{1}{27}$

Assume that we wish to construct an instantaneous *trinary* code for this source. First, we compute the entropy of the source (using trinary units to simplify arithmetic).

$$H_3 = \sum_{i=1}^{7} P_i \log_3 \frac{1}{P_i}$$
$$= \frac{13}{9} \text{ trinary units/symbol}$$

We know, therefore, that we cannot construct a trinary instantaneous code for this information source which uses fewer than $\frac{13}{9}$ trinary symbols per source symbol on the average. We can construct a code which does achieve exactly this value for L, however, since the P_i of this source are of the form $(\frac{1}{3})^{\alpha_i}$, with α_i integer. Using (4-9b) to find the required word lengths, we obtain the code

$s_1 \rightarrow 0$
$s_2 \rightarrow 1$
$s_3 \rightarrow 20$
$s_4 \rightarrow 21$
$s_5 \rightarrow 220$
$s_6 \rightarrow 221$
$s_7 \rightarrow 222$

As a check, we compute L:

$$L = \sum_{i=1}^{7} P_i l_i = \frac{13}{9} \text{ trinary symbols/source symbol}$$

4-3. Shannon's First Theorem

The coding problem for the zero-memory source with symbol probabilities of the form $(1/r)^{\alpha_i}$ has been solved. We now turn our attention to the zero-memory source with arbitrary symbol probabilities.

Equation (4-9b) tells us that if $\log_r (1/P_i)$ is an integer, we should choose the word length l_i equal to this integer. If $\log_r (1/P_i)$ is not an integer, it might seem reasonable that a compact code could be found by selecting l_i as the first integer greater than this value. This tempting conjecture is, in fact, not valid, but we shall find that selecting l_i in this manner can lead to some important results. We select l_i, therefore, as the unique integer satisfying

[handwritten: l_i as an integer must be between these two values that are not integers generally.]

$$\log_r \frac{1}{P_i} \leq l_i < \log_r \frac{1}{P_i} + 1 \tag{4-10}$$

First, we check to see that the word lengths chosen in this manner satisfy the Kraft inequality and are, therefore, acceptable as the word lengths of an instantaneous code. Taking exponentials of the left inequality of (4-10) leads to

$$\frac{1}{P_i} \leq r^{l_i}$$

or

$$P_i \geq r^{-l_i} \tag{4-11}$$

Summing (4-11) over all i, we obtain

$$1 \geq \sum_{i=1}^{q} r^{-l_i} \qquad \text{*[handwritten: which is Kraft]*}$$

Equation (4-10), therefore, defines an acceptable set of l_i for an instantaneous code.

If we multiply (4-10) by P_i and sum over all i, we find

$$H_r(S) \leq L < H_r(S) + 1 \tag{4-12}$$

Before proceeding, we should like to point out an important difference between (4-12) and the lower bound for L obtained in (4-7). Equations (4-7) express a bound for the average length L, independent of any particular coding scheme. The bound requires only that our code be instantaneous. Equation (4-12), on the other hand, was derived by assuming the coding method defined in (4-10). It provides both a lower and an upper bound on L *valid when we use the given coding method* (4-10).

Since (4-12) is valid for any zero-memory source, we may apply it to the *n*th extension of our original source S.

$$H_r(S^n) \leq L_n < H_r(S^n) + 1 \qquad (4\text{-}13)$$

L_n in (4-13) represents the average length of the code words corresponding to symbols from the *n*th extension of the source S. That is, if λ_i is the length of the code word corresponding to symbol σ_i, and $P(\sigma_i)$ is the probability of σ_i, then

q = # of alphabet symbols in Source

$$L_n = \sum_{i=1}^{q^n} P(\sigma_i)\lambda_i \qquad (4\text{-}14)$$

q^m = # of combinations of total of q symbols of n symbels at a time out

L_n/n, therefore, is the average number of code symbols† used per single symbol from S. From (2-16) we know that the entropy of S^n is n times the entropy of S. Equation (4-13) then may be written as

$$\boxed{H_r(S) \leq \frac{L_n}{n} < H_r(S) + \frac{1}{n}} \qquad (4\text{-}15a)$$

and so it is possible to make L_n/n as close to $H_r(S)$ as we wish by coding the *n*th extension of S rather than S:

$$\boxed{\lim_{n \to \infty} \frac{L_n}{n} = H_r(S)} \qquad (4\text{-}15b)$$

Equation (4-15a) is known as *Shannon's first theorem* or the *noiseless coding theorem*. It is one of the two major theorems of information theory. Equation (4-15a) tells us that we can make the average number of *r*-ary code symbols per source symbol as small as, but no smaller than, the entropy of the source measured in *r*-ary units. The price we pay for decreasing L_n/n is the increased

---

† Do not confuse the symbols L_n/n and L. They both refer to the average number of code symbols used per single source symbol. L_n/n, however, indicates that in order to obtain this average, we coded the source symbols s_i in blocks of n rather than singly.

coding complexity caused by the large number (q^n) of source symbols with which we must deal.

4-4. Shannon's First Theorem for Markov Sources

The results of the previous three sections may be extended to include the case of Markov sources. We provide the necessary proofs by applying our bounds on the average length to an appropriate adjoint source—a zero-memory source. Then we need only use the properties of adjoint sources as derived in Sections 2-6 and 2-7 to complete the proofs.

We define the first-order Markov source S, with source symbols $s_1, s_2, \ldots, s_q$ and conditional symbol probabilities $P(s_i/s_j)$. We also define S^n, the nth extension of S, with symbols $\sigma_1, \sigma_2, \ldots, \sigma_{q^n}$ and conditional symbol probabilities $P(\sigma_i/\sigma_j)$. We refer to the first-order (unconditional) symbol probabilities of S and S^n as P_i and $P(\sigma_i)$, respectively. The process of encoding the symbols $s_1, s_2, \ldots, s_q$ into an instantaneous block code is identical for the source S and its adjoint source $\bar{S}$. If the length of the code word corresponding to s_i is l_i, the average length of the code is [(4-1)]

$$L = \sum_{i=1}^{q} P_i l_i \qquad (4\text{-}16)$$

Furthermore, the average length is identical for S and $\bar{S}$ since P_i, the first-order symbol probability of s_i, is the same for both these sources. $\bar{S}$, however, is a *zero-memory* source, and we may apply (4-7c) to obtain

$$H_r(\bar{S}) \leq L \qquad (4\text{-}17)$$

This inequality may be augmented [(2-29)] to read

$$H_r(S) \leq H_r(\bar{S}) \leq L \qquad (4\text{-}18)$$

An analogous inequality may be written for S^n and $\overline{S^n}$.

$$H_r(S^n) \leq H_r(\overline{S^n}) \leq L_n \qquad (4\text{-}19)$$

L_n is the average length of a code word corresponding to one of the σ_i, as defined in (4-14).

Again, as in Section 4-3, we remark that these inequalities are completely general in that they do not depend upon the coding scheme we use. If we now select the l_i according to (4-10), we may bound L above and below (4-12),

$$H_r(\bar{S}) \leq L < H_r(\bar{S}) + 1 \qquad (4\text{-}20)$$

or, for the extended source,

$$H_r(\overline{S^n}) \leq L_n < H_r(\overline{S^n}) + 1 \qquad (4\text{-}21)$$

Using (2-41) and dividing by n yield

$$H_r(S) + \frac{H_r(\bar{S}) - H_r(S)}{n} \leq \frac{L_n}{n} < H_r(S) + \frac{[H_r(\bar{S}) - H_r(S)] + 1}{n} \qquad (4\text{-}22)$$

and so again we may make L_n/n as close to $H_r(S)$ as we wish by choosing n large enough—that is, by coding in long blocks. This is Shannon's first theorem for first-order Markov sources. The corresponding proof for mth-order Markov sources is not significantly different (Problem 4-1).

4-5. Coding without Extensions

Our proofs of Shannon's first theorem (for both the zero-memory and Markov cases) have been constructive. That is to say, (4-10) provides us with a method of choosing the word lengths l_i. If we use this method to choose word lengths of a block code for encoding the symbols from S^n, *and take n sufficiently large*, the quantity L_n/n can be made as close to $H_r(S)$ as we wish. What if we do not want to make n sufficiently large, however? For a *fixed n*, all the theorem tells us is that if we choose our word lengths according to (4-10), the average length will be no greater than the right side of (4-15a) [or (4-22)]. The theorem does not tell us what value of L (or L_n/n) we shall obtain. Even more important, it does *not* guarantee that choosing the word lengths according to (4-10) will give us the smallest possible value of L (or L_n/n) it is possible to obtain for that fixed n.

A simple example will serve to show that (4-10) may indeed provide a poor way to choose the word lengths. We use (4-10) to construct a binary instantaneous code for the zero-memory source defined in Table 4-4. Assume that we wish to encode this source directly without going to the second or higher extension. What is the smallest average length we can achieve without extensions?

To use (4-10) we first calculate $\log (1/P_i)$ as shown in the third column of Table 4-4. The length of the word corresponding to

TABLE 4-4. A CODING EXAMPLE

Source symbol	P_i	$\log \dfrac{1}{P_i}$	l_i	Code $\mathcal{C}$	Code $\mathcal{B}$
s_1	$\frac{2}{3}$	0.58	1	0	0
s_2	$\frac{2}{9}$	2.17	3	100	10
s_3	$\frac{1}{9}$	3.17	4	1010	11

S_i is then chosen to satisfy

$$\log \frac{1}{P_i} \leq l_i < \log \frac{1}{P_i} + 1$$

We have listed l_i in the fourth column of Table 4-4. Code $\mathcal{C}$, shown in column five, is then an acceptable instantaneous code with these word lengths. The average length of code $\mathcal{C}$ is

$$L_{\mathcal{C}} = \tfrac{2}{3} \times 1 + \tfrac{2}{9} \times 3 + \tfrac{1}{9} \times 4$$
$$= 1.78 \text{ binits/source symbol}$$

The entropy of the source is

$$H(S) = \sum_{i=1}^{3} P_i \log \frac{1}{P_i}$$
$$= 1.22 \text{ bits/source symbol}$$

Note that $L_{\mathcal{C}}$ is indeed bounded by

$$H(S) \leq L_{\mathcal{C}} < H(S) + 1 \tag{4-23}$$

This fact, however, is little consolation for a poor code. It is easy to find an instantaneous code for this source which is better than code $\mathcal{C}$. Such a code (code $\mathcal{B}$) is given in the last column of Table 4-4. For code $\mathcal{B}$ we calculate the average length

$$L_{\mathcal{B}} = \tfrac{2}{3} \times 1 + \tfrac{2}{9} \times 2 + \tfrac{1}{9} \times 2$$
$$= 1.33 \text{ binits/source symbol}$$

This number is a considerable improvement over the average length of code $\mathfrak{A}$. In addition, we see that in this case there is little to be gained by encoding the second (or higher) extension of our source. The best we could hope for is 1.22 binits per source symbol, and we have already achieved 1.33 binits per source symbol.

4-6. Finding Binary Compact Codes—Huffman Codes

If we wish to construct an instantaneous code for a given information source, we know that the average length of the code must be greater than or equal to the entropy of the source. From the example of Table 4-4, however, we see that the general coding methods we have developed so far lead to compact codes only in the limit as n, the order of the extension we consider, increases. How do we construct a compact code for a fixed source?

The question of the limiting value of L_n/n is of no relevance in the definition of compactness. A compact code for a source S is a code which has the smallest average length possible if we encode the symbols from S *one at a time.* In this section we develop a method of constructing compact codes for the case of a binary code alphabet. The more general problem of constructing compact codes for an r-ary code alphabet will be treated in Section 4-8. Both these problems were solved by Huffman (1952).

Consider the source S with symbols $s_1, s_2, \ldots, s_q$ and symbol probabilities $P_1, P_2, \ldots, P_q$. Let the symbols be ordered so that $P_1 \geq P_2 \geq \cdots \geq P_q$. By regarding the last two symbols of S as combined into one symbol, we obtain a new source† from S containing only $q - 1$ symbols. We refer to this new source as a *reduction* of S. The symbols of this reduction of S may be reordered, and again we may combine the two least probable symbols to form a reduction of this reduction of S. By proceeding in this manner, we construct a sequence of sources, each containing one fewer symbol than the previous one, until we arrive at a source with only two symbols.

Example 4-3. In Figure 4-1 we start with a source of six symbols and successively reduce this source to a source of two symbols.

† We take this source to be a zero-memory source for the sake of convenience. Since we are allowed to code only one symbol from S at a time, it does not make any difference whether S is a zero-memory or a Markov source.

Original source		Reduced sources			
Symbols	Probabilities	S_1	S_2	S_3	S_4
s_1	0.4	0.4	0.4	0.4	0.6
s_2	0.3	0.3	0.3	0.3	0.4
s_3	0.1	0.1	0.2	0.3	
s_4	0.1	0.1	0.1		
s_5	0.06	0.1			
s_6	0.04				

FIGURE 4-1. A source and its reductions.

Construction of a sequence of reduced sources, as illustrated, is the first step in the construction of a compact instantaneous code for the original source S. The second step is merely the recognition that a binary compact instantaneous code for the last reduced source (a source with only two symbols) is the trivial code with the two words 0 and 1. As the final step, we shall show that if we have a compact instantaneous code for one of the sources in the sequence of reduced sources, it is a simple matter to construct a compact instantaneous code for the source immediately preceding this reduced source. Using this fact, we start at the last reduced source and its trivial compact instantaneous code and work backward along the sequence of sources until we arrive at a compact instantaneous code for the original source.

Let us assume that we have found a compact instantaneous code for S_j, one of the sources in a sequence of reduced sources. One of the symbols of S_j, say s_α, is formed from *two* symbols of the preceding source S_{j-1}. We call these two symbols $s_{\alpha 0}$ and $s_{\alpha 1}$. Each of the other symbols of S_j corresponds to one of the remaining symbols of S_{j-1}. Then the compact instantaneous code for S_{j-1} is formed from the code for S_j as follows:

> We assign to each symbol of S_{j-1} (except $s_{\alpha 0}$ and $s_{\alpha 1}$) the code word used by the corresponding symbol of S_j. The code words used by $s_{\alpha 0}$ and $s_{\alpha 1}$ are formed by adding a 0 and 1, respectively, to the code word used for s_α. (4-24)

It is easy to see that the code we form in this manner is instantaneous [condition (3-1)]. The proof that the code is compact is not so immediate, and we defer the proof of this fact until after we have illustrated the construction of a compact code.

Example 4-4. We illustrate the synthesis of a binary compact code for the source of Figure 4-1.

Original source			Reduced sources			
Symbols	Probabilities	Code	S_1	S_2	S_3	S_4
s_1	0.4	1	0.4 1	0.4 1	0.4 1	0.6 0
s_2	0.3	00	0.3 00	0.3 00	0.3 00	0.4 1
s_3	0.1	011	0.1 011	0.2 010	0.3 01	
s_4	0.1	0100	0.1 0100	0.1 011		
s_5	0.06	01010	0.1 0101			
s_6	0.04	01011				

FIGURE 4-2. Synthesis of a compact code.

We formed the compact code shown at the left in the three steps previously noted. First, we formed a sequence of reduced sources from the original source S. (See also Figure 4-1.) Then we assigned the words 0 and 1 to the last source in the sequence (S_4 in this case). Finally, we worked our way back from S_4 to S through the reduced sources. As we passed from source to source, we "decomposed" one code word each time in order to form two new code words.

Several properties of compact codes are illustrated by this procedure. The multiplicity of compact codes is especially important. Note that the method used to form two words from one in passing from reduced source to reduced source is merely to add a binit to the end of the word we decompose. It makes no difference which of the two words formed is assigned to which of the source symbols. This means that the assignment of the two code symbols 0 and 1 to the various words of the compact code we construct is arbitrary. We may complement† the jth digit of every word of the code and obtain another compact code. For example, if we complement the first and last digits of the code of Figure 4-2, we have the "new" compact code:

† The complement of 0 is 1; the complement of 1 is 0.

0
10
111
1100
11011
11010

This method of producing a new compact code, however, results in just trivial differences in the two codes. The new code is obtained from the old code by a relabeling. It is also possible to obtain two compact codes for the same source which are fundamentally different. To see this, we synthesize a different code for the example given in Figure 4-2.

Example 4-5. We construct a different code for the source of Example 4-4 in Figure 4-3.

Original source			Reduced sources			
Sym- bols	Proba- bilities	Code	S_1	S_2	S_3	S_4
s_1	0.4	1	0.4 1	0.4 1	0.4 1	0.6 0
s_2	0.3	00	0.3 00	0.3 00	0.3 00⌐	0.4 1
s_3	0.1	0100	0.1 011	0.2 010⌐	0.3 01⌐	
s_4	0.1	0101	0.1 0100⌐	0.1 011⌐		
s_5	0.06	0110⌐	0.1 0101⌐			
s_6	0.04	0111⌐				

FIGURE 4-3. Synthesis of a compact code.

Note that the construction procedures indicated in Figures 4-2 and 4-3 are identical until we go from the code for S_1 to the code for the original source S. At that point we may decompose any one of the three words

011
0100
0101

If we choose the first of these words, we obtain a code with word lengths

1, 2, 4, 4, 4, 4

If we choose the second or the third, the word lengths obtained are

$$1, 2, 3, 4, 5, 5$$

The average lengths of the two codes obtained are identical:

$$L = 1(0.4) + 2(0.3) + 4(0.1) + 4(0.1) + 4(0.06) + 4(0.04)$$
$$= 2.2 \text{ binits/symbol}$$
$$L = 1(0.4) + 2(0.3) + 3(0.1) + 4(0.1) + 5(0.06) + 5(0.04)$$
$$= 2.2 \text{ binits/symbol}$$

and we cannot construct an instantaneous code for this source with a smaller average length.

Another point made evident by the synthesis procedure described is that it may sometimes be unnecessary to form a sequence of reductions of the original source all the way to a source with only two symbols.   This is so since we need only form reductions until we find the first reduction for which we have a compact code.   Once we have a compact code for any reduction of a source, we may start working backward from this compact code, as described in rule (4-24).   This point is illustrated in Figure 4-4.

	Original source		Reduced source
Symbols	Probabilities	Code	S_1
s_1	0.5	0	0.5 0
s_2	0.25	10	0.25 10
s_3	0.125	110	0.125 110
s_4	0.100	1110⌐ ┌►0.125 111
s_5	0.025	1111⌐

FIGURE 4-4. Synthesis of a compact code.

After forming the first reduction of this source, we see that all the symbol probabilities of the first reduction are of the form $(\frac{1}{2})^{\alpha_i}$, with α_i an integer.   We may then use the results of Section 4-2 to form a compact code for this reduction, and work backward to a compact code for the original source as before.

4-7. Completing the Proof

In the previous section we showed how to construct a compact code for an arbitrary information source. The proof of optimality was complete but for the demonstration that the code constructed from rule (4-24) is compact. We now provide this proof. Assume that we have found a compact code $\mathcal{C}_j$ for some reduction, say S_j, of an original source S. Let the average length of this code be L_j. One of the symbols of S_j, say s_α, is formed from the two least probable symbols of the preceding reduction S_{j-1}. Let these two symbols be $s_{\alpha 0}$ and $s_{\alpha 1}$, and let their probabilities be $P_{\alpha 0}$ and $P_{\alpha 1}$, respectively. The probability of s_α is then $P_\alpha = P_{\alpha 0} + P_{\alpha 1}$. Let the code for S_{j-1} formed according to rule (4-24) be called $\mathcal{C}_{j-1}$, and let its average length be L_{j-1}. L_{j-1} is easily related to L_j since the words of $\mathcal{C}_j$ and $\mathcal{C}_{j-1}$ are identical except that the (two) words for $s_{\alpha 0}$ and $s_{\alpha 1}$ are one binit longer than the (one) word for s_α. Thus we know that

$$L_{j-1} = L_j + P_{\alpha 0} + P_{\alpha 1} \tag{4-25}$$

We wish to show that if $\mathcal{C}_j$ is compact, then $\mathcal{C}_{j-1}$ must also be compact. In other words, if L_j is the smallest possible average length of an instantaneous code for S_j, then L_{j-1} [as given by Equation (4-25)] is the smallest possible average length for an instantaneous code for S_{j-1}. Again we provide a proof by demonstrating that assuming the contrary leads to a contradiction. Assume that we have found a compact code for S_{j-1} with average length $\tilde{L}_{j-1} < L_{j-1}$. Let the words of the code be $\tilde{X}_1$, $\tilde{X}_2$, . . . , $\tilde{X}_{\alpha 1}$ with lengths l_1, l_2, . . . , $l_{\alpha 1}$, respectively. We assume that the subscripts are ordered in order of decreasing symbol probabilities so that

$$l_1 \leq l_2 \leq \cdots \leq l_{\alpha 1}$$

One of the words of this code (call it $\tilde{X}_{\alpha 0}$) must be identical with $\tilde{X}_{\alpha 1}$ except in its last digit. If this were not true, we could drop the last digit from $\tilde{X}_{\alpha 1}$ and decrease the average length of the code without destroying its instantaneous property. Finally, we form $\tilde{\mathcal{C}}_j$, a code for S_j, by combining $\tilde{X}_{\alpha 1}$ and $\tilde{X}_{\alpha 0}$ and dropping their last binit while leaving all other words unchanged. This gives us an instantaneous code for S_j with average length $\tilde{L}_j$, related to $\tilde{L}_{j-1}$ by

$$\tilde{L}_{j-1} = \tilde{L}_j + P_{\alpha 0} + P_{\alpha 1} \tag{4-26}$$

This equation may be compared with (4-25). From these two equations, we see that our assumption $\tilde{L}_{j-1} < L_{j-1}$ implies that we may construct a code with average length $\tilde{L}_j < L_j$. This is the contradiction we seek since the code with average length L_j is compact.

Our proof that (4-24) leads from one compact code to another is complete. Before we consider the more general case of coding into an alphabet of r symbols, it might be well to point out two properties of compact codes we have discovered in passing. The first of these is simply that if the probabilities of the symbols of a source are ordered so that $P_1 \geq P_2 \geq \cdots \geq P_q$, the lengths of the words assigned to these symbols will be ordered so that $l_1 \leq l_2 \leq \cdots \leq l_q$. This is not surprising. It is merely an expression of the fact that we assign the shortest words to the most probable symbols of our code. The second property is perhaps a bit less obvious. We have shown that the lengths of the last two words (in order of decreasing probability) of a compact code are identical:

$$l_q = l_{q-1} \tag{4-27}$$

If there are several symbols with probability P_q, we may assign their subscripts so that the words assigned to the last two symbols differ only in their last digit.

4-8. r-ary Compact Codes

Section 4-6 pointed out that the construction of a binary compact code proceeded in three steps. First, we formed a sequence of reduced sources from the original source. Then we found a compact code for one of the sources in this sequence. Finally, we worked our way backward through the sequence, constructing new compact codes from the ones we had obtained, until we formed a compact code for the original source S. In this section we shall see that the construction of a compact code consists of the same three steps when the code alphabet has r symbols. The last two of these steps, furthermore, will be changed in no important respect from the binary case.

The formation of reduced sources preparatory to the synthesis of a *binary* compact code proceeded by combining the *two* least probable source symbols in order to form a single symbol. When we wish to form an r-ary compact code, we shall combine the source symbols r *at a time* in order to form one symbol in the reduced source. One hitch appears in the r-ary case, however, which did not appear in the binary case. In the binary case, each source in the sequence of reduced sources contained one fewer symbol than the source immediately preceding. In the r-ary case, we combine r symbols to form one symbol, and thus each source in the sequence has $r - 1$ fewer symbols than the preceding source. We would like the last source in the sequence to have exactly r symbols. (This will allow us to construct the trivial compact code for this source.) The last source will have r symbols if and only if the original source has $r + \alpha(r - 1)$ symbols, where α is an integer. Therefore, if the original source does not have $r + \alpha(r - 1)$ symbols, we add "dummy symbols" to the source until this number is reached. The dummy symbols are assumed to have probability 0, and so they may be ignored after a code is formed.

Example 4-6. Consider the source S with 11 symbols shown in Figure 4-5. We wish to form a sequence of reduced sources from this source before encoding the source in a quaternary code—a code using four code symbols. If the last source in the sequence is to have four symbols, S must have $4 + 3\alpha$ symbols, where α is an integer. Since 11 is not of the form $4 + 3\alpha$, we add two dummy symbols to S to bring the total number of symbols to 13. Now, reducing the source four symbols at a time produces a source with exactly four symbols.

$$\frac{q - r}{r - 1} = \alpha = integer$$

$$\frac{11 - 4}{3} = \frac{7}{3} \rightarrow \frac{9}{3}$$

	Original source		Reduced sources		
	Symbols	Probabilities	S_1	S_2	S_3
	s_1	0.22	0.22	0.23	0.40
	s_2	0.15	0.15	0.22	0.23
	s_3	0.12	0.12	0.15	0.22
	s_4	0.10	0.10	0.12	0.15
	s_5	0.10	0.10	0.10	
	s_6	0.08	0.08	0.10	
	s_7	0.06	0.07	0.08	
	s_8	0.05	0.06		
	s_9	0.05	0.05		
	s_{10}	0.04	0.05		
	s_{11}	0.03			
Dummy	s_{12}	0.00			
symbols	s_{13}	0.00			

FIGURE 4-5. A source and its reductions.

Having formed the reductions shown in Figure 4-5, we proceed to synthesize a compact code in the same manner as in Section 4-6. We assign r code words, each of length 1, to the last reduction in order to form a compact code for this source. This code is enlarged, just as in the binary case, to form a compact code for the preceding reduced source. Each time we go from a reduced source to the preceding reduced source, we form r symbols from one symbol for a net gain of $r - 1$ symbols. The proof that if we start with a compact code we shall produce a compact code by this procedure is entirely analagous to the proof provided in Section 4-7 (Problem 4-2).

Example 4-7. To provide an illustration of the procedure described above, we find a quaternary compact code (Figure 4-6) for the source of Figure 4-5.

	Original source		Reduced sources				
Symbol	Probability	Code word	S_1		S_2		S_3
s_1	0.22	2	0.22	2	0.23	1	0.40	0
s_2	0.15	3	0.15	3	0.22	2	0.23	1
s_3	0.12	00	0.12	00	0.15	3	0.22	2
s_4	0.10	01	0.10	01	0.12	00	0.15	3
s_5	0.10	02	0.10	02	0.10	01		
s_6	0.08	03	0.08	03	0.10	02		
s_7	0.06	11	0.07	10	0.08	03		
s_8	0.05	12	0.06	11				
s_9	0.05	13	0.05	12				
s_{10}	0.04	100	0.05	13				
s_{11}	0.03	101						
s_{12}	0.00	102						
s_{13}	0.00	103						

FIGURE 4-6. A quaternary compact code.

4-9. Code Efficiency and Redundancy

Shannon's first theorem shows that there exists a common yardstick with which we may measure any information source. The *value* of a symbol from an information source S may be measured in terms of an equivalent number of binary digits needed to repre-

it turned out that in a compact code
the more info a symbol contains (log $\frac{1}{p_i}$) the
more digits are needed to represent it.

86   INFORMATION THEORY AND CODING

sent one symbol from that source; the theorem says that the average value of a symbol from S is $H(S)$. More generally, the average value of a symbol from S in terms of r-ary digits is $H_r(S)$.

Let the average length of a uniquely decodable r-ary code for the source S be L. L cannot be less than $H_r(S)$. Accordingly, we define η, the *efficiency* of the code, by

$$\eta = \frac{H_r(S)}{L} \tag{4-28}$$

It is also possible to define the *redundancy* of a code.

measure of excess superfluity

Redundancy $= 1 - \eta$

$$= \frac{L - H_r(S)}{L} \tag{4-29}$$

Example 4-8.   Consider the zero-memory source $S = \{s_1, s_2\}$, with $P(s_1) = \frac{3}{4}$ and $P(s_2) = \frac{1}{4}$. We calculate

$$H(S) = \tfrac{1}{4} \log 4 + \tfrac{3}{4} \log \tfrac{4}{3}$$
$$= 0.811 \text{ bit}$$

A compact code for this source is as follows:

s_i	$P(s_i)$	Compact code
s_1	$\frac{3}{4}$	0
s_2	$\frac{1}{4}$	1

The average length of this code is 1 binit, and so the efficiency is

$$\eta_1 = 0.811$$

To improve the efficiency, we might code S^2, the second extension of S:

σ_i	$P(\sigma_i)$	Compact code
$s_1 s_1$	$\frac{9}{16}$	0
$s_1 s_2$	$\frac{3}{16}$	10
$s_2 s_1$	$\frac{3}{16}$	110
$s_2 s_2$	$\frac{1}{16}$	111

$$L = 1 \cdot \tfrac{9}{16} + 2 \cdot \tfrac{3}{16} + 3 \cdot \tfrac{3}{16} + 3 \cdot \tfrac{1}{16} = \frac{9+6+9+3}{16} = \frac{27}{16}$$

The average length of this code is $\frac{27}{16}$ binits.   The entropy of S^2 is $2H(S)$; so

$$\eta_2 = \frac{2 \times 0.811 \times 16}{27}$$
$$= 0.961$$

Coding the third and fourth extensions of S, we find efficiencies

$$\eta_3 = 0.985$$

and

$$\eta_4 = 0.991$$

As we encode higher and higher extensions of the original source S, the efficiency must approach 1.   In this example, the approach is quite rapid, and little increase in efficiency can be obtained by going further than the second extension.   Such behavior is typical of Huffman coding.

The previous example showed the increase in efficiency obtained by encoding higher and higher extensions of a source.   It will be instructive to examine the efficiency as a function of r, the number of symbols in the code alphabet.

Example 4-9.   We take a zero-memory source S with 13 symbols and symbol probabilities as shown in Table 4-5.   In the same table we list the compact (Huffman) code for code alphabets comprised of 2 to 13 symbols.

TABLE 4-5. COMPACT CODES FOR DIFFERENT CODE ALPHABETS

$P(s_i)$	s_i	\multicolumn{12}{c}{Compact codes for $r =$}
		13	12	11	10	9	8	7	6	5	4	3	2
$\frac{1}{4}$	s_1	0	0	0	0	0	0	0	0	0	0	0	00
$\frac{1}{4}$	s_2	1	1	1	1	1	1	1	1	1	1	1	01
$\frac{1}{16}$	s_3	2	2	2	2	2	2	2	2	2	20	200	1000
$\frac{1}{16}$	s_4	3	3	3	3	3	3	3	3	30	21	201	1001
$\frac{1}{16}$	s_5	4	4	4	4	4	4	4	4	31	22	202	1010
$\frac{1}{16}$	s_6	5	5	5	5	5	5	5	50	32	23	210	1011
$\frac{1}{16}$	s_7	6	6	6	6	6	6	60	51	33	30	211	1100
$\frac{1}{16}$	s_8	7	7	7	7	7	70	61	52	34	31	212	1101
$\frac{1}{16}$	s_9	8	8	8	8	80	71	62	53	40	32	220	1110
$\frac{1}{64}$	s_{10}	9	9	9	90	81	72	63	54	41	330	221	111100
$\frac{1}{64}$	s_{11}	A	A	A0	91	82	73	64	550	42	331	2220	111101
$\frac{1}{64}$	s_{12}	B	B0	A1	92	83	74	65	551	43	332	2221	111110
$\frac{1}{64}$	s_{13}	C	B1	A2	93	84	75	66	552	44	333	2222	111111
Average length L...		1	$\frac{33}{32}$	$\frac{67}{64}$	$\frac{17}{16}$	$\frac{9}{8}$	$\frac{19}{16}$	$\frac{5}{4}$	$\frac{87}{64}$	$\frac{23}{16}$	$\frac{25}{16}$	$\frac{131}{64}$	$\frac{25}{8}$

The entropy of the source of Table 4-5 is 3.125 bits per symbol. Using this fact and (4-28), we may plot the efficiency as a function of r.

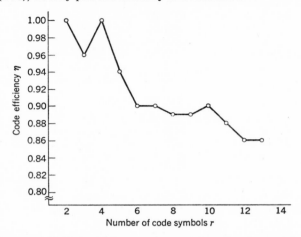

FIGURE 4-7. Code efficiency versus number of code symbols.

From Figure 4-7 we see that the efficiency tends to climb as r decreases. The increase in efficiency, however, is not monotonic. Note the efficiency of the code for $r = 2$ and $r = 4$. The symbol probabilities are all of the form $1/2^\alpha$ or $1/4^\alpha$, where α is an integer. In these cases, we know (Section 4-2) that we can find a compact code with average length equal to the entropy.

NOTES

Note 1. In this chapter we have proved Shannon's first theorem only for ergodic Markov sources with a finite number of symbols (i.e., states). A more elegant proof of this theorem, valid for any stationary, ergodic source, was given by McMillan (1953) in a slightly different form, called the asymptotic equipartition property (AEP). For a general source S, let

$$I(s_1, s_2, \ldots, s_n) = \log \frac{1}{P(s_1, s_2, \ldots, s_n)}$$

S has the AEP if $I(s_1, s_2, \ldots, s_n)/n$ converges in probability to $H(S)$. The importance of the AEP lies in the fact that long sequences of outputs from a source with this property can be divided into two classes:

1. A class such that each sequence in the class has probability roughly equal to $2^{-nH(S)}$

2. A class composed of sequences which hardly ever occur

A simple combinatorial proof of the AEP has been provided by Thomasian

(1960).   A generalization to more complicated sources is given by Perez (1959).

Note 2.   In Section 4-6 we provided an example to show that two different (in their word lengths) binary codes might each be compact for a given source. Golomb has investigated the conditions under which this phenomenon can occur and the number of different possible nontrivially different compact codes for a given source.

We can describe the construction of a code by means of a code tree (Fano, 1961).   For example, consider the binary code and its corresponding tree.

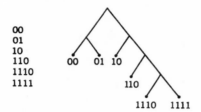

00
01
10
110
1110
1111

Then the question of how many different codes exist for a source with q symbols can be phrased in terms of code trees.

For $q = 2$ there is only one possible tree corresponding to the word lengths.

$$l_1 = 1$$
$$l_2 = 1$$

For $q = 3$ there is again only one possible tree corresponding to the word lengths.

$$l_1 = 1$$
$$l_2 = 2$$
$$l_3 = 2$$

For $q = 4$ there are two possible trees.

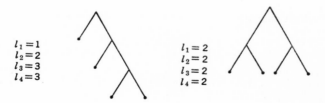

$$l_1 = 1$$
$$l_2 = 2$$
$$l_3 = 3$$
$$l_4 = 3$$

$$l_1 = 2$$
$$l_2 = 2$$
$$l_3 = 2$$
$$l_4 = 2$$

For $q = 5$ there are three possible trees.

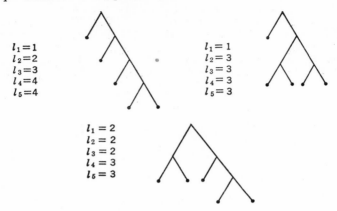

$l_1 = 1$
$l_2 = 2$
$l_3 = 3$
$l_4 = 4$
$l_5 = 4$

$l_1 = 1$
$l_2 = 3$
$l_3 = 3$
$l_4 = 3$
$l_5 = 3$

$l_1 = 2$
$l_2 = 2$
$l_3 = 2$
$l_4 = 3$
$l_5 = 3$

For $q = 6$ and 7 there are five and nine different trees, respectively.

Golomb has also found conditions on the symbol probabilities in order for more than one compact code to exist. For example, with $q = 4$, we must clearly have $P_1 = P_3 + P_4$. Further analysis shows that $\frac{1}{3} \leq P_1 \leq \frac{2}{5}$ if two different compact codes exist.

Note 3. We have treated the problem of coding information sources under the assumption that the duration (or some other criterion of cost) is the same for each code symbol. When this is not the case, certain modifications of the results of Chapter 4 are required. Let the code alphabet be

$$X = \{x_1, x_2, \ldots , x_r\}$$

and let the duration of code symbol x_i be t_i. Then if $N(T)$ is the number of sequences of duration exactly T,

$$N(T) = N(T - t_1) + N(T - t_2) + \cdots + N(T - t_r)$$

When this difference equation is solved, we find that $N(T)$ grows as $A R_0{}^T$ for large T, where A is some constant and R_0 is the largest real root of the characteristic equation

$$z^{-t_1} + z^{-t_2} + \cdots + z^{-t_r} - 1 = 0$$

The asymptotic number of equivalent binits per unit time is then

$$\lim_{T \to \infty} \frac{\log N(T)}{T} = R_0$$

and this result can be used to modify our form of Shannon's first theorem.

The problem of finite time coding for such a code alphabet (equivalent to Huffman coding) has been treated by Karp (1961).

PROBLEMS

4-1. Prove Equation (4-22) for mth-order Markov sources.

4-2. Show that proceeding from reduced source to reduced source, as described in Section 4-8, will produce an r-ary compact code, if one starts with an r-ary compact code.

4-3. A sequence of symbols from S^n is coded by the Huffman procedure into a code alphabet $X = \{x_1, x_2, \ldots, x_r\}$. The result of this coding procedure may be viewed as a new information source with the source alphabet X. Show that the probability of each of the symbols x_i of this new source approaches $1/r$ as n increases.

4-4. A zero-memory binary source has $P(0) = 0.1$ and $P(1) = 0.9$.

(a) Find $H(S)$.

(b) Find L, the average word length of a compact code for S when $X = \{0, 1\}$.

(c) Find L_n/n for $n = 2, 3, 4$ and $n \to \infty$, when S^n is encoded into a compact code, still with $X = \{0, 1\}$.

(d) Find the efficiency of your four codes.

4-5. In Problem 4-4 we encoded S, S^2, S^3, and S^4 into X. These codings produced sequences of 0s and 1s. We can view these sequences as being emitted from some new source S_0, as shown in Figure P 4-5. Find $H(\bar{S}_0)$ when $n = 1, 2, 3, 4$.

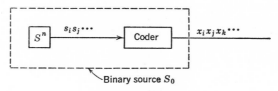

FIGURE P 4-5

4-6. Given the following table:

S	s_1	s_2	s_3	s_4	s_5	s_6	s_7
$P(s_i)$	$\frac{1}{3}$	$\frac{1}{3}$	$\frac{1}{9}$	$\frac{1}{9}$	$\frac{1}{27}$	$\frac{1}{27}$	$\frac{1}{27}$

(a) Find $H(S)$ and $H_3(S)$.

(b) Find a compact code for $H(S)$ when $X = \{0, 1\}$ and $X = \{0, 1, 2\}$.

(c) Compute L for both the above codes.

4-7. Given the following table:

S	s_1	s_2	s_3	s_4	s_5	s_6	s_7	s_8
$P(s_i)$	0.4	0.2	0.1	0.1	0.05	0.05	0.05	0.05

(a) Find a compact code for this source with $X = \{0, 1, 2\}$.

(b) There may be more than one nontrivially different (i.e., different sets of word lengths) compact code for this source and this alphabet. List the sets of word lengths for all such codes you can find.

4-8. Let $\epsilon = \frac{1}{2}$ in Problem 2-14. A binary code is found for S with $L = H(S)$. Find L', the average length of a compact code for S'.

4-9. The source S has nine symbols; each occurs with probability $\frac{1}{9}$.

(a) Find a compact code for S using the code alphabet $X = \{0, 1\}$.

(b) Find a compact code for S using the code alphabet $X = \{0, 1, 2\}$.

(c) Find a compact code for S using the code alphabet $X = \{0, 1, 2, 3\}$.

4-10. A source S has six symbols with probabilities P_1 to P_6, respectively. Assume that we have ordered the P_i so that $P_1 \geq P_2 \geq \cdots \geq P_6$. We wish to find a compact code for this source using the code alphabet $X = \{0, 1, 2, 3\}$. Find a set of word lengths for such a compact code if $P_6 = \frac{1}{64}$.

4-11. Find all possible different compact binary codes for the source shown in the following table:

S	s_1	s_2	s_3	s_4	s_5	s_6	s_7	s_8	s_9	s_{10}
$P(s_i)$	0.20	0.18	0.12	0.10	0.10	0.08	0.06	0.06	0.06	0.04.

Count as "different" codes only those codes with different sets of word lengths l_i

4-12. (a) Find the five different code trees corresponding to $q = 6$ in Note 2.

(b) Find the nine different code trees corresponding to $q = 7$.

4-13. This problem deals with a generalization of Note 2. Find all possible different code trees corresponding to *trinary* compact codes for sources with $q = 3, 4, 5, 6, 7, 8, 9$.

5

CHANNELS AND MUTUAL INFORMATION

5-1. Introduction

In the first four chapters, we were concerned with properties of information sources and with transformations of sequences of source symbols into sequences of code symbols. We were able to relate our information measure to properties of information sources. In particular, the entropy of a source (expressed in suitable units) was shown to define a lower bound to the average number of code symbols needed to encode each source symbol. We used this bound in Section 4-9 to define the efficiency and redundancy of a

93

code. Indeed, in retrospect we note that a large portion of the first part of this book was devoted to providing a background for our definitions of efficiency and redundancy and to the synthesis of codes containing as little redundancy as possible.

In view of this preoccupation with redundancy reduction up to now, it may surprise the reader to learn that Chapters 5 and 6 will be concerned primarily with methods of putting redundancy back into codes! We shall see that it is not always desirable to use codes with little or no redundancy. In this chapter, our interest will shift from the information *source* to the information *channel*—that is, from information generation to information transmission.

Our introduction of the concept of an information channel leads directly to the possibility of errors arising in the process of information transmission. We shall study the effect such errors have on our efforts to transmit information. This will, in turn, lead to the possibility of coding in order to decrease the effect of errors caused by an information channel. The reader should not be surprised to learn that our information measure may be used to analyze this type of coding, as well as the type of coding already discussed. In fact, in spite of the considerable progress we have made so far, the central result of information theory and the most dramatic use of the concept of entropy are yet to come. This result—Shannon's remarkable second theorem—will use the entropy idea to describe how we may utilize an *unreliable* information channel to transmit *reliable* information!

5-2. Information Channels

Our primary concern in the rest of this book will be the information channel.

> *Definition.* An *information channel*† is described by giving an input alphabet $A = \{a_i\}$, $i = 1, 2, \ldots, r$; an output alphabet $B = \{b_j\}$, $j = 1, 2, \ldots, s$; and a

† The channel defined above is sometimes called a zero-memory information channel. A more general definition, where the probability of a given output y_j may depend upon several preceding input symbols or even output symbols, is also possible. Such channels are referred to as channels with memory.

set of conditional probabilities $P(b_j/a_i)$ for all i and j. $P(b_j/a_i)$ is just the probability that the output symbol b_j will be received if the input symbol a_i is sent.

A particular channel of great theoretical and practical importance is the binary symmetric channel (BSC).

The channel diagram of the BSC is shown in Figure 5-2. As usual, we let $\bar{p} = 1 - p$. This channel has two input symbols ($a_1 = 0$, $a_2 = 1$) and two output symbols ($b_1 = 0$, $b_2 = 1$). It is symmetric because the probability of receiving a 1 if a 0 is sent is

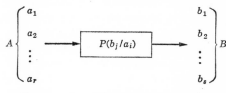

FIGURE 5-1. An information channel.   FIGURE 5-2. The binary symmetric channel (BSC).

equal to the probability of receiving a 0 if a 1 is sent; this probability, the probability that an error will occur, is p.

A convenient way of describing an information channel is to arrange the conditional probabilities of its outputs as shown in Figure 5-3.

Outputs

		b_1	b_2	$\cdots$	b_s
	a_1	$P(b_1/a_1)$	$P(b_2/a_1)$	$\cdots$	$P(b_s/a_1)$
Inputs	a_2	$P(b_1/a_2)$	$P(b_2/a_2)$	$\cdots$	$P(b_s/a_2)$
$\cdots$					
	a_r	$P(b_1/a_r)$	$P(b_2/a_r)$	$\cdots$	$P(b_s/a_r)$

FIGURE 5-3. Description of an information channel.

Note that each row of this array corresponds to a fixed input, and that the terms in this row are just the probabilities of obtaining the various b_j at the output if that fixed input is sent. We shall see this description of an information channel so often that it will be useful to have a more streamlined notation for it. Accordingly, we define

$$P_{ij} = P(b_j/a_i) \qquad (5\text{-}1)$$

send   *receive*

and the array of Figure 5-3 becomes the channel matrix $\mathbf{P}$:

$$\mathbf{P} = \begin{bmatrix} P_{11} & P_{12} & \cdots & P_{1s} \\ P_{21} & P_{22} & \cdots & P_{2s} \\ \cdots\cdots\cdots\cdots\cdots\cdots \\ P_{r1} & P_{r2} & \cdots & P_{rs} \end{bmatrix} \tag{5-2}$$

An information channel is completely described by giving its channel matrix. We therefore use $\mathbf{P}$ interchangeably to represent both the channel matrix and the channel.

Each row of the channel matrix corresponds to an input of our channel, and each column corresponds to a channel output. Note a fundamental property of the channel matrix—the terms in any one row of the matrix must sum to 1.† This follows since, if we send any input symbol a_i, we must get *some* output symbol. We write this equation for future reference:

$$\sum_{j=1}^{s} P_{ij} = 1 \qquad i = 1, 2, \ldots, r \tag{5-3}$$

The channel matrix of the BSC is

$$\begin{bmatrix} \bar{p} & p \\ p & \bar{p} \end{bmatrix} \tag{5-4}$$

Just as we did in the case of information sources, we may view the inputs and outputs of a channel in blocks of n symbols, rather than individually. Thus, we define the nth extension of a channel.

> *Definition.* Consider an information channel with input alphabet $A = \{a_i\}$, $i = 1, 2, \ldots, r$; output alphabet $B = \{b_j\}$, $j = 1, 2, \ldots, s$; and channel matrix
>
> $$\mathbf{P} = \begin{bmatrix} P_{11} & P_{12} & \cdots & P_{1s} \\ P_{21} & P_{22} & \cdots & P_{2s} \\ \cdots\cdots\cdots\cdots\cdots\cdots\cdots \\ P_{r1} & P_{r2} & \cdots & P_{rs} \end{bmatrix}$$
>
> The nth extension of this channel has input alphabet $A^n = \{\alpha_i\}$, $i = 1, 2, \ldots, r^n$; output alphabet $B^n = \{\beta_j\}$, $j = 1, 2, \ldots, s^n$; and channel matrix

† Such matrices are called *Markov matrices* or *stochastic matrices*.

$$\Pi = \begin{bmatrix} \Pi_{11} & \Pi_{12} & \cdots & \Pi_{1s^n} \\ \Pi_{21} & \Pi_{22} & \cdots & \Pi_{2s^n} \\ \cdots\cdots\cdots\cdots\cdots\cdots \\ \Pi_{r^n1} & \Pi_{r^n2} & \cdots & \Pi_{r^ns^n} \end{bmatrix}$$

Each of the inputs α_i consists of a sequence of n elementary input symbols $(a_{i1}, a_{i2}, \ldots, a_{in})$, and each of the outputs β_j consists of a sequence of n elementary output symbols $(b_{j1}, b_{j2}, \ldots, b_{jn})$. The probability $\Pi_{ij} = P(\beta_j/\alpha_i)$ consists of the product of the corresponding elementary symbol probabilities.

Just as was the case when we defined the extension of an information source, the extension of an information channel is not really a new concept, but just a new way of viewing an old concept. Merely by looking at symbols of some channel in blocks of length n, we obtain the nth extension of that channel.

Example 5-1. The second extension of the BSC is a channel with four input symbols and four output symbols. Its channel matrix is shown in Figure 5-4.

$$\Pi = \begin{bmatrix} \bar{p}^2 & \bar{p}p & p\bar{p} & p^2 \\ \bar{p}p & \bar{p}^2 & p^2 & p\bar{p} \\ p\bar{p} & p^2 & \bar{p}^2 & \bar{p}p \\ p^2 & p\bar{p} & \bar{p}p & \bar{p}^2 \end{bmatrix}$$

FIGURE 5-4. Channel matrix of the (BSC)².

We note that the channel matrix of the (BSC)² may be written as a matrix of matrices. Let **P**, as before, be the channel matrix of the BSC. Then, the channel matrix of the (BSC)² can also be written

$$\Pi = \begin{bmatrix} \bar{p}\mathbf{P} & p\mathbf{P} \\ p\mathbf{P} & \bar{p}\mathbf{P} \end{bmatrix}$$

The above matrix is known as the *Kronecker square* (Bellman, 1960) (or tensor square) of the matrix **P**. In the more general case the channel matrix of the nth extension of a channel is the nth Kronecker power of the original channel matrix.

In the first part of the book, we used our information measure to measure the average amount of information produced by a source. The function of an information channel, however, is not to produce information, but to transmit information from the input to the output. We expect, therefore, to use our information measure to measure the ability of a channel to transport information. This will indeed be the case; we now proceed to an investigation of the amount of information a channel can transmit.

5-3. Probability Relations in a Channel

Consider an information channel with r input symbols and s output symbols. We define the channel by the channel matrix $\mathbf{P}$:

$$\mathbf{P} = \begin{bmatrix} P_{11} & P_{12} & \cdots & P_{1s} \\ P_{21} & P_{22} & \cdots & P_{2s} \\ \cdots & \cdots & \cdots & \cdots \\ P_{r1} & P_{r2} & \cdots & P_{rs} \end{bmatrix} \tag{5-5}$$

Let us select input symbols according to the probabilities $P(a_1)$, $P(a_2), \ldots, P(a_r)$ for transmission through this channel. Then the output symbols will appear according to some other set of probabilities: $P(b_1), P(b_2), \ldots, P(b_s)$. The relations between the probabilities of the various input symbols and the probabilities of the various output symbols are easily derived. For example, there are r ways in which we might receive output symbol b_1. If a_1 is sent, b_1 will occur with probability P_{11}; if a_2 is sent, b_1 will occur with probability P_{21}; etc. We therefore write

$$P(a_1)P_{11} + P(a_2)P_{21} + \cdots + P(a_r)P_{r1} = P(b_1) \tag{5-6a}$$
$$P(a_1)P_{12} + P(a_2)P_{22} + \cdots + P(a_r)P_{r2} = P(b_2) \tag{5-6b}$$
$$\cdots\cdots\cdots\cdots\cdots\cdots\cdots\cdots\cdots$$
$$P(a_1)P_{1s} + P(a_2)P_{2s} + \cdots + P(a_r)P_{rs} = P(b_s) \tag{5-6c}$$

Equations (5-6) provide us with expressions for the probabilities of the various output symbols if we are given the input probabilities $P(a_i)$ and the channel matrix, the matrix of conditional probabilities $P(b_j/a_i)$. For the remainder of this chapter, we assume that we are given the $P(a_i)$ and the $P(b_j/a_i)$, so that the $P(b_j)$ may be calculated from (5-6). Note, however, that if we are given the *output* probabilities $P(b_j)$ and $P(b_j/a_i)$, it may not be possible to invert the system of linear equations (5-6) in order to determine the $P(a_i)$. For example, in a BSC with $p = \frac{1}{2}$, any set of input probabilities will lead to output symbols which are equiprobable. In general, there may be many input distributions which lead to the same output distribution. If we are given the input distribution, on the other hand, we may always calculate a unique output distribution with the aid of (5-6).

In addition to the $P(b_j)$, there are two more sets of probabilities associated with an information channel which may be calculated from the $P(a_i)$ and the $P(b_j/a_i)$. According to Bayes' law, the conditional probability of an input a_i, given that an output b_j has been received, is

$$P(a_i/b_j) = \frac{P(b_j/a_i)P(a_i)}{P(b_j)} \qquad (5\text{-}7a)$$

or, using (5-6),

$$P(a_i/b_j) = \frac{P(b_j/a_i)P(a_i)}{\sum_{i=1}^{r} P(b_j/a_i)P(a_i)} \qquad (5\text{-}7b)$$

The probabilities $P(a_i/b_j)$ are sometimes referred to as *backward probabilities* in order to distinguish them from the *forward probabilities* $P(b_j/a_i)$.

The numerator of the right side of (5-7) is the probability of the joint event (a_i, b_j),

$$P(a_i, b_j) = P(b_j/a_i)P(a_i) \qquad (5\text{-}8a)$$

and this quantity may also be recognized as

$$P(a_i, b_j) = P(a_i/b_j)P(b_j) \qquad (5\text{-}8b)$$

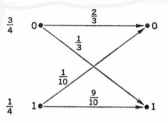

FIGURE 5-5. A noisy information channel.

Example 5-2. Let us illustrate the calculation of the various probabilities associated with an information channel. We take a binary channel; that is, $A = \{0, 1\}$ and $B = \{0, 1\}$. We assume that the $P(b_j/a_i)$ are as shown in the channel matrix

$$\mathbf{P} = \begin{bmatrix} \frac{2}{3} & \frac{1}{3} \\ \frac{1}{10} & \frac{9}{10} \end{bmatrix}$$

We associate the rows and columns of the above matrix with the input and output symbols in the natural order. Therefore Pr $\{b = 0/a = 0\} = \frac{2}{3}$, Pr $\{b = 1/a = 0\} = \frac{1}{3}$, etc. Finally, we assume that Pr $\{a = 0\} = \frac{3}{4}$ and Pr $\{a = 1\} = \frac{1}{4}$. The information given above is neatly summarized in Figure 5-5.

The probabilities of the output symbols are obtained with the use of (5-6).

$$\text{Pr }\{b = 0\} = (\tfrac{3}{4})(\tfrac{2}{3}) + (\tfrac{1}{4})(\tfrac{1}{10}) = \tfrac{21}{40} \tag{5-9a}$$

$$\text{Pr }\{b = 1\} = (\tfrac{3}{4})(\tfrac{1}{3}) + (\tfrac{1}{4})(\tfrac{9}{10}) = \tfrac{19}{40} \tag{5-9b}$$

As a check, we note that $\text{Pr }\{b = 0\} + \text{Pr }\{b = 1\} = 1$. The conditional input probabilities are obtained from (5-7).

$$\text{Pr }\{a = 0/b = 0\} = \frac{(\tfrac{3}{4})(\tfrac{2}{3})}{(\tfrac{21}{40})} = \tfrac{20}{21} \tag{5-10a}$$

$$\text{Pr }\{a = 1/b = 1\} = \frac{(\tfrac{1}{4})(\tfrac{9}{10})}{(\tfrac{19}{40})} = \tfrac{9}{19} \tag{5-10b}$$

The other two backward probabilities may be similarly obtained. A simpler method, however, is to use the fact that $\text{Pr }\{a = 0/b = 0\} + \text{Pr }\{a = 1/b = 0\} = 1$ and $\text{Pr }\{a = 0/b = 1\} + \text{Pr }\{a = 1/b = 1\} = 1$. Thus,

$$\text{Pr }\{a = 1/b = 0\} = \tfrac{1}{21} \tag{5-10c}$$

$$\text{Pr }\{a = 0/b = 1\} = \tfrac{10}{19} \tag{5-10d}$$

The probabilities of various joint events are found by using (5-8). We calculate just one of these:

$$\begin{aligned}
\text{Pr }\{a = 0, b = 0\} &= \text{Pr }\{a = 0/b = 0\} \text{ Pr }\{b = 0\} \\
&= (\tfrac{20}{21})(\tfrac{21}{40}) \\
&= \tfrac{1}{2}
\end{aligned} \tag{5-11}$$

5-4. A Priori and A Posteriori Entropies

The various output symbols of our channel occur according to the set of probabilities $P(b_j)$. Note that the probability a given output symbol will be b_j is $P(b_j)$ *if* we do not know which input symbol is sent. On the other hand, if we do know that input symbol a_i is sent, the probability that the corresponding output will be b_j changes from $P(b_j)$ to $P(b_j/a_i)$. Likewise, we recall that the input symbol a_i is chosen with probability $P(a_i)$. If we observe the output symbol b_j, however, we know the probability that a_i is the corresponding input symbol is $P(a_i/b_j)$ [(5-7)]. Let us focus our attention on this change induced on the probabilities of the various input symbols by the reception of a given output symbol b_j.

We shall refer to the $P(a_i)$ as the *a priori* probabilities of the input symbols—the probabilities of the a_i before the reception of an output symbol. The $P(a_i/b_j)$ will be called the *a posteriori* probabilities of the input symbols—the probabilities after the reception of b_j.   From Section 2-2 we know that we can calculate the entropy of the set of input symbols with respect to both these sets of probabilities.   The *a priori entropy* of A is†

$$H(A) = \sum_A P(a) \log \frac{1}{P(a)} \tag{5-12}$$

and the *a posteriori entropy* of A, when b_j is received, is

$$H(A/b_j) = \sum_A P(a/b_j) \log \frac{1}{P(a/b_j)} \tag{5-13}$$

The interpretation of these two quantities follows directly from Shannon's first theorem. $H(A)$ is the average number of binits needed to represent a symbol from a source with the a priori probabilities $P(a_i)$, $i = 1, 2, \ldots, r$; $H(A/b_j)$ is the average number of binits needed to represent a symbol from a source with the a posteriori probabilities $P(a_i/b_j)$, $i = 1, 2, \ldots, r$.

Example 5-3.   We repeat, as Figure 5-6, the figure used in Example 5-2 for ease of reference.   The a priori entropy of the set of input symbols is

$$H(A) = \tfrac{3}{4}\log\tfrac{4}{3} + \tfrac{1}{4}\log 4 = 0.811 \text{ bit} \tag{5-14}$$

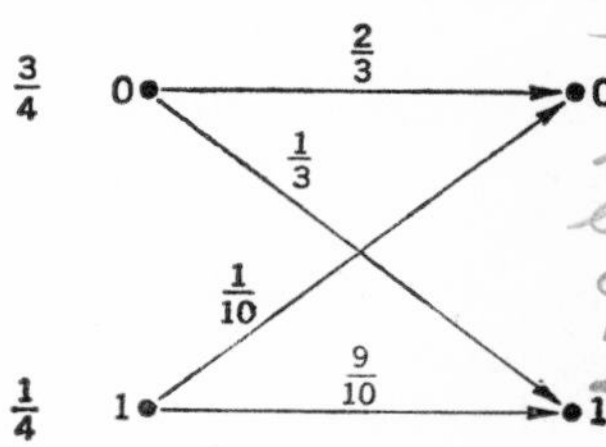

FIGURE 5-6. A noisy information channel.

If we receive the symbol 0 at the output of the channel, our a posteriori probabilities will be given by (5-10a) and (5-10b). The a posteriori entropy is

$$H(A/0) = \tfrac{20}{21}\log\tfrac{21}{20} + \tfrac{1}{21}\log 21 = 0.276 \text{ bit} \tag{5-15}$$

If we receive the symbol 1, on the other hand, the a posteriori entropy is

$$H(A/1) = \tfrac{9}{19}\log\tfrac{19}{9} + \tfrac{10}{19}\log\tfrac{19}{10} = 0.998 \text{ bit} \tag{5-16}$$

Hence, if a 0 is received, the entropy—our uncertainty about which input was sent—decreases, whereas if a 1 is received, our uncertainty increases.

5-5. A Generalization of Shannon's First Theorem

Shannon's first theorem tells us that the entropy of an alphabet may be interpreted as the average number of binits necessary to

† In the remainder of this book it will be convenient to omit the subscripts from a_i and b_j when writing sums over all symbols of the A or B alphabets.

represent one symbol of that alphabet.   Consider this interpretation applied to the a priori and a posteriori entropies (Figure 5-7).

Before reception of the output symbol of the channel, we associate the a priori probabilities $P(a_i)$ with the input alphabet A. The average number of binits necessary to represent a symbol from this alphabet is $H(A)$.   If we receive

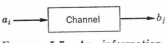

a given symbol, say b_j, we associate the a posteriori probabilities $P(a_i/b_j)$

FIGURE 5-7.   An information channel.

with the input alphabet.   The average number of binits necessary to represent a symbol from the alphabet with these (a posteriori) statistics is $H(A/b_j)$.   Since the output symbols occur with probabilities $P(b_j)$, we might expect that the average number of binits (now averaged over b_j also) necessary to represent an input symbol a_i, if we are given an output symbol, is the average a posteriori entropy,

$$\sum_B P(b)H(A/b) \tag{5-17}$$

This important result is, in fact, true.   It does not follow from Shannon's first theorem, however.   That theorem deals only with coding for a source with a fixed set of source statistics and not with coding for a source which selects a new set of source statistics after each output symbol.   We therefore generalize Shannon's first theorem to cover this case.

The question we ask in order to obtain such a generalization is the same question we asked in order to obtain Shannon's first theorem, namely, "What is the most efficient method of coding from a source?"   (In this case, the source is A.)   This time, however, the statistics of the source we wish to code change from symbol to symbol.   The indication of which set of source statistics we have is provided by the output of the channel b_j.   Since a compact code for one set of source statistics will not, in general, be a compact code for another set of source statistics, we take advantage of our knowledge of b_j for each transmitted symbol to construct s binary[†] codes—one for each of the possible received symbols b_j.   When the output of our channel is b_j, we use the jth binary code to encode the transmitted symbol a_i.   Let the word lengths of our s codes be as shown in Table 5-1.

[†] The binary assumption is not necessary, but it serves to simplify the discussion which follows.

TABLE 5-1. WORD LENGTHS FOR s CODES

Input symbol	Code 1	Code 2	$\cdots$	Code s
a_1	l_{11}	l_{12}	$\cdots$	l_{1s}
a_2	l_{21}	l_{22}	$\cdots$	l_{2s}
$\cdots$	$\cdots$	$\cdots$	$\cdots$	$\cdots$
a_r	l_{r1}	l_{r2}	$\cdots$	l_{rs}

[handwritten: r sent symbols] *[handwritten: red l_1]* *[handwritten: s received symbols]*

If we require these codes to be instantaneous, we may apply the first part of Shannon's first theorem (4-7) to each code separately and obtain

$$H(A/b_j) \leq \sum_A P(a_i/b_j)l_{ij} \triangleq L_j \qquad (5\text{-}18)$$

L_j is the average length of the jth code. We employ the conditional probabilities $P(a_i/b_j)$ rather than the marginal probabilities $P(a_i)$ to calculate L_j, since the jth code is employed only when b_j is the received symbol. The average number of binits used for each member of the A alphabet when we encode in this fashion is obtained by averaging with respect to the received symbols b_j. Multiplying (5-18) by $P(b_j)$ and summing over all B yield

$$\sum_B H(A/b_j)P(b_j) \leq \sum_{A,B} P(a_i, b_j)l_{ij} \triangleq \bar{L} \qquad (5\text{-}19)$$

where $\bar{L}$ is the average number of binits per symbol from the A alphabet—averaged with respect to both input and output symbols. Note the similarity of (5-19) to (4-7).

In order to show that the bound (5-19) can be achieved, we next describe a specific coding procedure. When b_j is the output of our channel, we select l_{ij}, the word length of the code word corresponding to the input a_i, as the unique integer satisfying

$$\log \frac{1}{P(a_i/b_j)} \leq l_{ij} < \log \frac{1}{P(a_i/b_j)} + 1 \qquad (5\text{-}20)$$

Word lengths defined in this fashion satisfy the Kraft inequality† for each j. The l_{ij}, therefore, define s sets of word lengths acceptable as the word lengths of s instantaneous codes. Now multiply

† This can be shown in exactly the same manner used in our proof of Shannon's first theorem (Section 4-3).

(5-20) by $P(a_i, b_j) = P(a_i/b_j)P(b_j)$,

$$P(b_j)P(a_i/b_j) \log \frac{1}{P(a_i/b_j)} \leq l_{ij}P(a_i, b_j)$$
$$< P(b_j)P(a_i/b_j) \log \frac{1}{P(a_i/b_j)} + P(a_i, b_j) \quad (5\text{-}21)$$

and sum this equation over all members of the A and B alphabets:

$$\sum_B P(b)H(A/b) \leq \bar{L} < \sum_B P(b)H(A/b) + 1 \quad (5\text{-}22)$$

Equation (5-22) is valid for any channel of the type we have considered. In particular, it is valid for the nth extension of the original channel,

$$\sum_{B^n} P(\beta)H(A^n/\beta) \leq \overline{L_n} < \sum_{B^n} P(\beta)H(A^n/\beta) + 1 \quad (5\text{-}23)$$

where $\overline{L_n}$ is the average word length of a symbol from A^n, or, equivalently, the average word length of n symbols from A. Each a posteriori entropy $H(A^n/\beta)$ in (5-23) can be written as the sum of n terms of the form $H(A/b)$, so that (5-23) becomes

$$\boxed{\sum_B P(b)H(A/b) \leq \frac{\overline{L_n}}{n} < \sum_B P(b)H(A/b) + \frac{1}{n}} \quad (5\text{-}24)$$

and (5-24) is the generalization of Shannon's first theorem we seek. Note the similarity of (5-24) to (4-15a). By increasing n, we may make $\overline{L_n}/n$ as close to

$$\sum_B P(b)H(A/b) \quad (5\text{-}25)$$

as we want. $\overline{L_n}/n$ is the average number of binits needed to encode a symbol from the input alphabet A if we already have the corresponding symbol from the output alphabet B. *or better, assuming*

$\overline{L_n}$ of (5-24) is measured in binits, and $H(A/b_j)$ is measured in bits; it is trivial to generalize this expression so that $\overline{L_n}$ is measured in r-ary symbols and $H(A/b_j)$ is measured in r-ary information units.

Up to this point, we have refrained from simplifying

$$\sum_B P(b)H(A/b)$$

in order to emphasize the fact that it is an average of the a posteriori entropies.   Now we define

$$H(A/B) = \sum_B P(b)H(A/b)$$

$$= \sum_B P(b) \sum_A P(a/b) \log \frac{1}{P(a/b)}$$

$$= \sum_{A,B} P(a, b) \log \frac{1}{P(a/b)} \qquad (5\text{-}26)$$

$H(A/B)$ is called the *equivocation* (of A with respect to B), or sometimes the channel *equivocation*.   In terms of the equivocation, we may write (5-24) as

$$\lim_{n \to \infty} \frac{\overline{L_n}}{n} = H(A/B) \qquad (5\text{-}27)$$

We have taken such pains to emphasize the similarities between the proof of (5-24) and the proof of Shannon's first theorem that the reader may not have noticed one major difference.   Successive input symbols a_i (or blocks of input symbols) are encoded, using different codes corresponding to the different output symbols b_j (or blocks of output symbols) occurring.   Even though each of the codes used is uniquely decodable, it is not generally true that a sequence of code words from a known sequence of uniquely decodable codes is uniquely decodable.   It is not sufficient, therefore, to select a set of *uniquely decodable* codes with word lengths satisfying (5-20); the codes must all be *instantaneous*.   In summary, we remark that (5-24) applies only to instantaneous codes, whereas Shannon's first theorem applies to all uniquely decodable codes, instantaneous or not. *In other words several uniquely decod. code sequences may not result in uniquely decodable sequences when put together unless they are all instantaneous*

5-6. Mutual Information

Let us return to the consideration of an information channel with r inputs and s outputs (Figure 5-8).

If the inputs are selected according to the probabilities $P(a_i)$, $i = 1, 2, \ldots, r$, the entropy of the input alphabet is

$$H(A) = \sum_A P(a) \log \frac{1}{P(a)} \qquad (5\text{-}28)$$

If we have the input probabilities and the forward probabilities $P(b_j/a_i)$, we may calculate (Section 5-3) the backward probabilities $P(a_i/b_j)$, the joint probabilities $P(a_i, b_j)$, and thus the equivocation

(through the output probs.)

$$H(A/B) = \sum_{A,B} P(a, b) \log \frac{1}{P(a/b)} \qquad (5\text{-}29)$$

By Shannon's first theorem we need an average of $H(A)$ binits to specify one input symbol a_i. By the generalization of Section 5-5, we need only an average of $H(A/B)$ binits to specify one input symbol, *if we are allowed to observe the output symbol produced by*

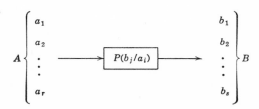

FIGURE 5-8. An information channel.

that input. It is natural to say, therefore, that, on the average, observation of a single output symbol provides us with $[H(A) - H(A/B)]$ bits of information. This difference is called the *mutual information* (of A and B), or the mutual information of the channel. It is written

ave info per input symbol gained by

$$I(A; B) = H(A) - H(A/B) \qquad (5\text{-}30)$$

observing one output symbol

We now develop several alternative ways of writing the mutual information,

$$
\begin{aligned}
I(A; B) &= H(A) - H(A/B) \\
&= \sum_{A} P(a) \log \frac{1}{P(a)} - \sum_{A,B} P(a, b) \log \frac{1}{P(a/b)} \\
&= \sum_{A,B} P(a, b) \log \frac{1}{P(a)} - \sum_{A,B} P(a, b) \log \frac{1}{P(a/b)} \\
&= \sum_{A,B} P(a, b) \log \frac{P(a/b)}{P(a)} \qquad (5\text{-}31a)
\end{aligned}
$$

$H(A) = \sum_A P(a) \log \frac{1}{P(a)} \cdot \sum_B P(b/a) = \sum_{AB} \frac{P(a)P(b/a)}{P(a,b)}$

or, since

$$P(a_i, b_j) = P(a_i/b_j)P(b_j)$$

$$I(A;B) = \sum_{A,B} P(a, b) \log \frac{P(a, b)}{P(a)P(b)} \qquad (5\text{-}31b)$$

The mutual information of the nth extension of a channel may be calculated from (5-31a). If the symbols of A^n are selected according to $P(\alpha_i) = P(a_{i_1})P(a_{i_2}) \cdots P(a_{i_n})$, the mutual information of the nth extension is just n times the mutual information of the original channel (Problem 5-4):

$$I(A^n;B^n) = nI(A;B) \qquad (5\text{-}32)$$

5-7. Properties of Mutual Information

We have shown that the mutual information is equal to the average number of binits necessary to specify an input symbol before receiving an output symbol less the average number of binits necessary to specify an input symbol after receiving an output symbol. That is,

$$I(A;B) = H(A) - H(A/B) \qquad (5\text{-}33)$$

An immediate question raised by this interpretation of mutual information is that of its sign. We have already noted (Section 5-4) that $H(A) - H(A/b_j)$ may be negative; the entropy of the input alphabet may be greater after reception of a particular output symbol b_j. The mutual information is just the average (over all output symbols) of $H(A) - H(A/b_j)$, however. Can this average be negative? To answer, we rewrite (5-31b):

$$I(A;B) = \sum_{A,B} P(a, b) \log \frac{P(a, b)}{P(a)P(b)} \qquad (5\text{-}31b)$$

A direct application of inequality (2-8a) then yields

$$I(A;B) \geq 0 \qquad (5\text{-}34)$$

with equality if, and only if, *as then the requirement for $\geq \& \leq$ are fulfilled*

$$P(a_i, b_j) = P(a_i)P(b_j) \qquad \text{for all } i, j \qquad (5\text{-}35)$$

This is a reassuring result. It says the average information received through a channel is always nonnegative. We cannot lose information, on the average, by observing the output of a channel. Furthermore, *the only condition under which the average information is zero occurs when the input and output symbols are statistically independent* [(5-35)].

Another important property of the mutual information may be seen by inspection of (5-31b). This equation, which we may take as the definition of $I(A\,;B)$, is symmetric in the two random variables a_i and b_j. Interchanging the roles of the input and output symbols leaves $I(A\,;B)$ unchanged. We may therefore write

$$I(A\,;B) = I(B\,;A) \tag{5-36}$$

an equation which emphasizes the mutuality of mutual information. Carrying this argument even further, we rewrite (5-33) as

$$I(A\,;B) = H(B) - H(B/A) \tag{5-37}$$

where

$$H(B) = \sum_B P(b) \log \frac{1}{P(b)} \tag{5-38}$$

and

$$H(B/A) = \sum_{A,B} P(a,\,b) \log \frac{1}{P(b/a)} \tag{5-39}$$

This last quantity is called the equivocation of B with respect to A.

In addition to the entropies $H(A)$ and $H(B)$, it is possible to define a joint entropy which measures the uncertainty of the joint event $(a_i,\,b_j)$. The probability of this event is $P(a_i,\,b_j)$, so that the joint entropy is

$$H(A,\,B) = \sum_{A,B} P(a,\,b) \log \frac{1}{P(a,\,b)} \tag{5-40}$$

The relationship of $H(A,\,B)$ to $H(A)$ and $H(B)$ is easily derived.

$$
\begin{aligned}
H(A,\,B) &= \sum_{A,B} P(a,\,b) \log \frac{P(a)P(b)}{P(a,\,b)} + \sum_{A,B} P(a,\,b) \log \frac{1}{P(a)P(b)} \\
&= -I(A\,;B) + \sum_{A,B} P(a,\,b) \log \frac{1}{P(a)} \\
&\qquad\qquad\qquad + \sum_{A,B} P(a,\,b) \log \frac{1}{P(b)} \\
&= -I(A\,;B) + \sum_A P(a) \log \frac{1}{P(a)} + \sum_B P(b) \log \frac{1}{P(b)} \\
&= H(A) + H(B) - I(A\,;B) \tag{5-41}
\end{aligned}
$$

The joint entropy of A and B, $H(A, B)$, is, of course, symmetric in A and B.

An easy method of recalling the various relationships we have derived is given in the diagram of Figure 5-9.

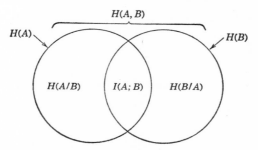

FIGURE 5-9. Relationships among some channel quantities.

The entropy of A is represented by the circle on the left, and the entropy of B by the circle on the right. The overlap between the two circles is the mutual information, so that the remaining portions of $H(A)$ and $H(B)$ represent the equivocations.

$$H(A/B) = H(A) - I(A;B) \qquad (5\text{-}42)$$
$$H(B/A) = H(B) - I(A;B) \qquad (5\text{-}43)$$

The joint entropy $H(A, B)$ is the sum of $H(A)$ and $H(B)$ except for the fact that the overlap is included twice, so that

$$H(A, B) = H(A) + H(B) - I(A;B) \qquad (5\text{-}44)$$

Also note

$$H(A, B) = H(A) + H(B/A) \qquad (5\text{-}45a)$$

and

$$H(A, B) = H(B) + H(A/B) \qquad (5\text{-}45b)$$

These equations follow directly from (5-42), (5-43), and (5-44), or by inspection of Figure 5-9. We may interpret these equations as saying that the total uncertainty in both A and B is either the sum of the uncertainty in A plus the uncertainty in B after we are given A, or vice versa.

Finally, although our primary interest is in information channels, we note that the arguments used in this section do not depend upon the fact that A is the input alphabet and B is the output alphabet of an information channel. We may define the information measures shown in Figure 5-9 for any two sets of random variables. If the sets of random variables are not statistically independent, they will have a positive mutual information.

Example 5-4. We compute the mutual information for a BSC. The channel matrix of the BSC is

$$\begin{bmatrix} \bar{p} & p \\ p & \bar{p} \end{bmatrix}$$

where $\bar{p} = 1 - p$. Assume that the probabilities of a 0 and a 1 being transmitted are ω and $\bar{\omega}$, respectively. We write the mutual information in the form

$$
\begin{aligned}
I(A;B) &= H(B) - H(B/A) \\
&= H(B) - \sum_A P(a) \sum_B P(b/a) \log \frac{1}{P(b/a)} \\
&= H(B) - \sum_A P(a) \left(p \log \frac{1}{p} + \bar{p} \log \frac{1}{\bar{p}} \right) \\
&= H(B) - \left(p \log \frac{1}{p} + \bar{p} \log \frac{1}{\bar{p}} \right) \tag{5-46}
\end{aligned}
$$

The probabilities that $b_j = 0$ and $b_j = 1$ are easily calculated to be $\omega \bar{p} + \bar{\omega} p$

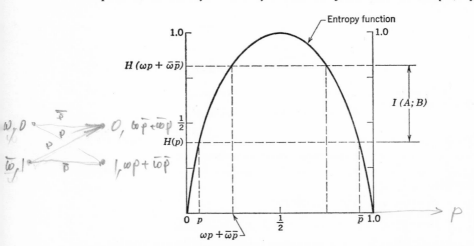

FIGURE 5-10. Geometric interpretation of the mutual information of a BSC.

and $\omega p + \bar{\omega} \bar{p}$, respectively. Hence

$$
I(A;B) = \left[(\omega \bar{p} + \bar{\omega} p) \log \frac{1}{\omega \bar{p} + \bar{\omega} p} + (\omega p + \bar{\omega} \bar{p}) \log \frac{1}{\omega p + \bar{\omega} \bar{p}} \right] \\
- \left(p \log \frac{1}{p} + \bar{p} \log \frac{1}{\bar{p}} \right) \tag{5-47}
$$

We may write $I(A; B)$ in terms of the entropy function (Figure 2-3)

$$I(A; B) = H(\omega p + \bar{\omega} \bar{p}) - H(p) \qquad (5\text{-}48)$$

Equation (5-48) has a simple geometric interpretation. Since $\omega p + \bar{\omega} \bar{p}$ must *see* always lie between p and $\bar{p}$, $H(\omega p + \bar{\omega} \bar{p}) \geq H(p)$, and Figure 5-10 provides a *comment* geometric proof of the nonnegativity of mutual information.

Certain limiting conditions of interest may also be seen from Figure 5-10. For example, for a fixed value of p, we may vary ω and examine the behavior of $I(A; B)$. We see that $I(A; B)$ achieves its maximum when $\omega = \frac{1}{2}$, and the value of this maximum is $1 - H(p)$. For $\omega = 0$ or $\omega = 1$, on the other hand, the mutual information is 0.

5-8. Noiseless Channels and Deterministic Channels

In this section, we define two special types of channels and obtain simplified expressions for the mutual information of these channels.

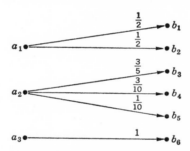

FIGURE 5-11. A noiseless channel.

In the discussion that follows, we assume that each column of the channel matrix has at least one nonzero element. An output symbol corresponding to a column of zeros will occur with probability 0 for any distribution over the input symbols. It is therefore of no interest and may be ignored.

> *Definition.* A channel described by a channel matrix with one, and only one, nonzero element in each column will be called a *noiseless channel.*

Example 5-5. The channel matrix of a noiseless channel is given as

$$\mathbf{P} = \begin{bmatrix} \frac{1}{2} & \frac{1}{2} & 0 & 0 & 0 & 0 \\ 0 & 0 & \frac{3}{5} & \frac{3}{10} & \frac{1}{10} & 0 \\ 0 & 0 & 0 & 0 & 0 & 1 \end{bmatrix}$$

The channel diagram of this channel is shown in Figure 5-11.

A BSC with probability of error p equal to 0 is a noiseless channel. Note, however, that a BSC with probability of error equal to 1 is also a noiseless channel! This is an expression of the fact that a channel which is consistently in error can be as useful as a channel which is consistently correct.

> *Definition.* A channel described by a channel matrix with one, and only one, nonzero element in each row will be called a *deterministic channel.*

Example 5-6. The channel matrix of a deterministic channel is given as

$$P = \begin{bmatrix} 1 & 0 & 0 \\ 1 & 0 & 0 \\ 0 & 1 & 0 \\ 0 & 1 & 0 \\ 0 & 1 & 0 \\ 0 & 0 & 1 \end{bmatrix}$$

each input symbol has a determine output symbol, it may be the so as the output of other inpu

The channel diagram of this channel is shown in Figure 5-12.

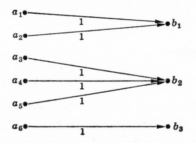

FIGURE 5-12. A deterministic channel.

Since there is but one nonzero element in each row of a deterministic channel matrix, and the sum of the elements in each row must be 1, the elements of a deterministic channel matrix are all either 0 or 1.

The mutual information of the types of channels defined above can be easily calculated. First, consider a noiseless channel. In a noiseless channel, when we observe the output b_j, we know with probability 1 which a_i was transmitted—that is, the conditional probabilities $P(a_i/b_j)$ are all either 0 or 1. Now, we write the equivocation $H(A/B)$ as

$$H(A/B) = \sum_B P(b_j) \sum_A P(a_i/b_j) \log \frac{1}{P(a_i/b_j)} \qquad (5\text{-}49)$$

and we note that all the terms in the inner summation (being either of the form $1 \times \log 1$ or $0 \times \log \frac{1}{0}$) are zero. Hence, for a noiseless channel,

$$H(A/B) = 0 \tag{5-50}$$

This conclusion is also evident in view of the generalization of Shannon's first theorem (Section 5-5). The outputs of a noiseless channel are sufficient by themselves to specify the inputs to the channel. Hence, the average number of binits necessary to specify the inputs when we know the outputs is zero. From (5-30) we see that, for a noiseless channel,

$$I(A; B) = H(A) \tag{5-51}$$

The amount of information transmitted through such a channel is equal to the total uncertainty of the input alphabet.

For deterministic channels, we may derive a set of analogous results. In a deterministic channel, the *input* symbol a_i is sufficient to determine the *output* symbol b_j with probability 1. Hence, all the probabilities $P(b_j/a_i)$ are either 0 or 1, and

$$\begin{aligned} H(B/A) &= \sum_A P(a_i) \sum_B P(b_j/a_i) \log \frac{1}{P(b_j/a_i)} \\ &= 0 \end{aligned} \tag{5-52}$$

On using (5-37), we have, for a deterministic channel,

$$I(A; B) = H(B) \tag{5-53}$$

5-9. Cascaded Channels

Some interesting properties of entropy and mutual information are revealed by consideration of the cascade of two channels (Figure 5-13). [A detailed investigation of cascades of binary channels is provided by Silverman (1955).]

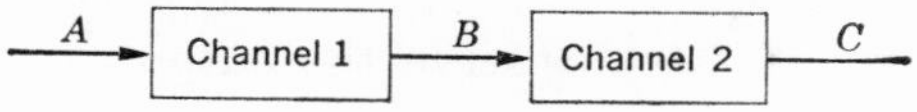

FIGURE 5-13. The cascade of two channels.

We assume that a channel with an r-symbol input alphabet A and an s-symbol output alphabet B is cascaded with a second channel, as indicated above. The input alphabet of the second

$Pb = \sum_A Pa\, P b/a \qquad Pc = \sum_B Pb\, P c/b = \sum_{AB} Pa\, P b/a\, P c/b$

$Pc_1 = Pc_1/b_1\, Pa_1\, Pb_1/a_1 + Pc_1/b_1\, Pa_2\, Pb_1/a_2 + Pc_1/b_2\, Pa_1\, Pb_2/a_1 + Pc_1/b_2\, Pa_2\, Pb_2/a_2$

channel is identified with B, and its output alphabet, consisting of t symbols, is denoted by C.

The fact that the alphabets are connected by the cascade of Figure 5-13 implies certain relationships among the symbol probabilities. When a_i, a symbol from A, is transmitted, the output of the first channel is some symbol from B, say b_j. In turn, b_j produces an output c_k from the second channel. The symbol c_k depends on the original input a_i only through b_j. In fact, if we know the intermediate symbol b_j, the probability of obtaining the terminal symbol c_k depends only upon b_j, and not upon the initial symbol a_i which produced b_j. This property of cascaded channels may be written as

$$P(c_k/b_j, a_i) = P(c_k/b_j) \qquad \text{for all } i, j, k \qquad (5\text{-}54)$$

Indeed, (5-54) may be taken as the definition of what we mean by the cascade of two channels. A direct application of Bayes' rule to (5-54) yields a similar equation in the reverse direction:

$$P(a_i/b_j, c_k) = P(a_i/b_j) \qquad (5\text{-}55)$$

It should be emphasized at this point that (5-54) and (5-55) hold only in the special case where A, B, and C are the alphabets of cascaded channels, as indicated in Figure 5-13.

As we transmit information through cascaded channels from A to B to C, it seems plausible that the equivocation should increase—that is, $H(A/C)$ should be greater than $H(A/B)$. Let us investigate this question. *because when going thru 2 channels the probabilities get more compressed to equalized hence entropy gets closer to it maximum when they are equiprobable*

$$H(A/C) - H(A/B) = \sum_{A,C} P(a, c) \log \frac{1}{P(a/c)}$$

H(A/B) gives info lost due to noisy channel usually all channel are noisy. loss of info occurs in each channel hence less in two > than loss in only one channel

$$- \sum_{A,B} P(a, b) \log \frac{1}{P(a/b)}$$

$$= \sum_{A,B,C} P(a, b, c) \log \frac{1}{P(a/c)}$$

$$- \sum_{A,B,C} P(a, b, c) \log \frac{1}{P(a/b)}$$

$$= \sum_{A,B,C} P(a, b, c) \log \frac{P(a/b)}{P(a/c)} \qquad (5\text{-}56)$$

Generally this would indicate that the info gained by the first transmission is partially lost by the second, because H(A/C) is info remaining in A after receiving C is > H(A)

Now we use (5-55) in (5-56):

$$H(A/C) - H(A/B) = \sum_{A,B,C} P(a, b, c) \log \frac{P(a/b, c)}{P(a/c)}$$

$$= \sum_{B,C} P(b, c) \sum_A P(a/b, c) \log \frac{P(a/b, c)}{P(a/c)} \quad (5\text{-}57)$$

We may use the inequality (2-8a) to show that the summation over the A alphabet in (5-57) is nonnegative. Hence,

$$H(A/C) - H(A/B) \geq 0 \qquad (5\text{-}58)$$

or

$$H(A/C) \geq H(A/B) \qquad (5\text{-}59)$$

An immediate consequence of (5-59) is

$$I(A; B) \geq I(A; C) \qquad (5\text{-}60)$$

These useful inequalities were apparently first proved by Woodward (1955). They show that information channels tend to "leak" information. The information that finally comes out of a cascade of channels can be no greater than the information which would emerge from an intermediate point in the cascade if we could tap such a point.

The condition for equality to hold in (5-59) and (5-60) is of some interest. Retracing the steps in our proof to (5-59), we see that the equality holds if, and only if,

$$P(a/b, c) = P(a/c) \qquad (5\text{-}61a)$$

for all a symbols and all b and c symbols, such that $P(b, c) \neq 0$. Equivalently, the condition may also be written as

$$P(a/b) = P(a/c) \qquad (5\text{-}61b)$$

for all a symbols and all b and c symbols, such that $P(b, c) \neq 0$.

The condition for equality deserves some comment. At first glance, it might appear that the equality would apply if, and only if, the second channel in the cascade of Figure 5-13 were noiseless. If this channel is noiseless, it is not hard to check that our condition (5-61b) will apply. That condition, however, will also apply in other circumstances, as the next example shows.

Example 5-7. Let us cascade the channel

$$\begin{bmatrix} \frac{1}{3} & \frac{1}{3} & \frac{1}{3} \\ 0 & \frac{1}{2} & \frac{1}{2} \end{bmatrix}$$

with the channel

$$\begin{bmatrix} 1 & 0 & 0 \\ 0 & \frac{2}{3} & \frac{1}{3} \\ 0 & \frac{1}{3} & \frac{2}{3} \end{bmatrix}$$

A channel diagram of the cascade is shown in Figure 5-14.

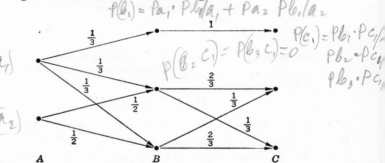

FIGURE 5-14. Cascaded channels.

In spite of the fact that neither channel is noiseless, it may be seen that (5-61b) holds, and, hence,

$$I(A; B) = I(A; C)$$

In this example, (5-61b) holds for *any* assignment of probabilities over the input alphabet A. It is also possible to find cases where (5-61b) holds only for some specific input distribution. We shall go into this point further in the next section.

We can illustrate the loss of information as it flows through a cascade of channels by employing people as information channels. A message, originally written in English, is translated into another language, and then translated back into English by a second translator who has not seen the original message. The result of this process will be a corrupted version of the original message, and may be thought of as the result of passing a message through a noisy channel. In order to simulate a cascade of channels, we repeat the process, this time, however, starting with the corrupted version of the message.

The experiment just described was performed using a simple four-line poem, The Turtle, by Ogden Nash.   The poem was translated from English to French to English to German to English to Spanish to English.   No effort was made to retain the rhyme or meter of the original piece.

> The turtle lives 'twixt plated decks
> Which practically conceal its sex.
> I think it clever of the turtle
> In such a fix to be so fertile.

The output of the English-French-English channel was

> The turtle lives in a scaled carapace which in fact hides its sex. I find that it is clever for the turtle to be so fertile in such a tricky situation.

The output of the English-German-English channel was

> The turtle lives in an enclosed shell under which, in reality, it hides its sex.   I find that the turtle must be very clever, indeed, to be so fertile in such a tight situation.

Finally, the output of the English-Spanish-English channel was

> The turtle lives inside a closed shell, under which, really, it hides its sex.   I feel the turtle had to be certainly clever to be so fertile in a so tight situation.

The noisiness of the human communication channel and the resulting loss of information have been recognized for some time. Thucydides, in Book I of "The Peloponnesian War," states:

Of the events of war, I have not ventured to speak from any chance information, nor according to any notion of my own [i.e., a priori probabilities]; I have described nothing but what I saw myself, or learned from others of whom I made the most careful and particular inquiry [i.e., noiseless channels].   The task was a laborious one, because eyewitnesses of the same occurrence gave different accounts of them, as they remembered or were interested in the actions of one side or the other [i.e., noisy channels].

As a final (but more quantitative) example of the loss of information in cascaded channels, we consider the case of the cascade of two identical BSCs.

Example 5-8. Two BSCs, each with channel matrix

$$\begin{bmatrix} \bar{p} & p \\ p & \bar{p} \end{bmatrix}$$

are cascaded as follows:

$$\xrightarrow{A}\boxed{\text{BSC}}\xrightarrow{B}\boxed{\text{BSC}}\xrightarrow{C}$$

The two possible inputs to the first BSC are chosen with equal probability. Hence, from (5-48) we have

because $\quad w = \bar{w} = \frac{1}{2}$ $\qquad I(A\,;\,B) \;=\; 1\,-\,H(p) \;=\; max.$ $\qquad$ (5-62)

It is easy to show that the cascade of these BSCs is equivalent to a single BSC with probability of error $2p\bar{p}$. Hence,

$$I(A\,;\,C) \;=\; 1\,-\,H(2p\bar{p}) \tag{5-63}$$

If another identical BSC is added (with output alphabet D), we obtain

$$I(A\,;\,D) \;=\; 1\,-\,H(3\bar{p}^2 p\,+\,p^3) \tag{5-64}$$

These curves are plotted in Figure 5-15.

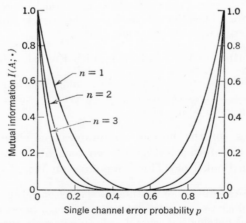

FIGURE 5-15. Mutual information of the cascade of n BSCs.   (Input symbols are assumed equally probable.)

5-10. Reduced Channels and Sufficient Reductions

In many types of information channels encountered in real life, the set of channel outputs is far larger than the user would like. For example, scientific data relayed from a satellite via a binary telemetry channel often contains information irrelevant to the primary phenomenon under investigation.   The antenna on the earth in such a system might obtain a sequence of pulses of various amplitudes.   The receiver would take each pulse and, if its amplitude is greater than some threshold, interpret the pulse as a "1"; if the amplitude is less than the threshold, the receiver interprets the pulse as a "0."   We may think of two different channels in the situation just described.   First, there is the channel with binary inputs (sent from the satellite) and a large number of outputs (corresponding to the number of distinguishable pulse amplitudes). Second, there is the channel with binary inputs and binary outputs (corresponding to the outputs of our receiver).   This second channel is clearly a simplification of the first channel; we call the second channel a *reduction* of the first.

Definition.   Consider a channel with r inputs and s outputs described by a channel matrix **P**.

$$\mathbf{P} = \begin{bmatrix} P_{11} & P_{12} & \cdots & P_{1i} & P_{1,i+1} & \cdots & P_{1s} \\ P_{21} & P_{22} & \cdots & P_{2i} & P_{2,i+1} & \cdots & P_{2s} \\ \multicolumn{7}{c}{\cdots\cdots\cdots\cdots\cdots\cdots\cdots\cdots\cdots\cdots} \\ P_{r1} & P_{r2} & \cdots & P_{ri} & P_{r,i+1} & \cdots & P_{rs} \end{bmatrix}$$

We define a new channel with r inputs and $s - 1$ outputs by adding together any two columns of **P**.   We call the channel matrix of the new channel **P′**.

$$\mathbf{P'} = \begin{bmatrix} P_{11} & P_{12} & \cdots & P_{1i} + P_{1,i+1} & \cdots & P_{1s} \\ P_{21} & P_{22} & \cdots & P_{2i} + P_{2,i+1} & \cdots & P_{2s} \\ \multicolumn{6}{c}{\cdots\cdots\cdots\cdots\cdots\cdots\cdots\cdots\cdots\cdots} \\ P_{r1} & P_{r2} & \cdots & P_{ri} + P_{r,i+1} & \cdots & P_{rs} \end{bmatrix}$$

The new channel **P′** is called an *elementary reduction* of **P**. We may repeat this process a number of times, forming an elementary reduction of **P′**, etc.   The end product of more than one elementary reduction will be called simply a *reduction* of the original channel **P**.

Example 5-9.   In Example 5-1 we formed the channel matrix of the (BSC)^2:

$$\mathbf{P} = \begin{bmatrix} \bar{p}^2 & \bar{p}p & p\bar{p} & p^2 \\ \bar{p}p & \bar{p}^2 & p^2 & p\bar{p} \\ p\bar{p} & p^2 & \bar{p}^2 & \bar{p}p \\ p^2 & p\bar{p} & \bar{p}p & \bar{p}^2 \end{bmatrix}$$

An elementary reduction of **P** is formed by combining the first and second columns:

$$\mathbf{P'} = \begin{bmatrix} \bar{p} & p\bar{p} & p^2 \\ \bar{p} & p^2 & p\bar{p} \\ p & \bar{p}^2 & p\bar{p} \\ p & \bar{p}p & \bar{p}^2 \end{bmatrix}$$

A reduction of **P** is formed by combining the second and third columns of **P'**:

$$\mathbf{P''} = \begin{bmatrix} \bar{p} & p \\ \bar{p} & p \\ p & \bar{p} \\ p & \bar{p} \end{bmatrix}$$

A useful way of viewing a reduced channel is as shown in Figure 5-16. The deterministic channel combines symbols of the B alpha-

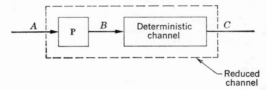

FIGURE 5-16. A reduced channel.

bet into a smaller number of symbols of the C alphabet. Hence, the channel with input alphabet A and output alphabet C indicated by dashed lines in Figure 5-16 is a reduction of channel **P**. This method of constructing a reduced channel allows us to use the results of the previous section on channel cascades. In particular, we have (referring to Figure 5-16)

$$H(A/C) \geq H(A/B) \qquad (5\text{-}65)$$

and

$$I(A;C) \leq I(A;B) \qquad (5\text{-}66)$$

Forming a reduction of a channel decreases (or at best leaves unchanged) the mutual information of the input and output alphabets. This is the price we pay for simplification in the channel.

A most important question suggested by the above remarks is, "When can we simplify the channel without paying a penalty in reduced mutual information?" That is, "When is the mutual information of a reduced channel equal to that of the original channel?" In order to answer this question, we need only consider the case of elementary reductions. The question in the case of a general reduction may then be answered by induction.

Let us form an elementary reduction of the channel

$$\mathbf{P} = \begin{bmatrix} P_{11} & P_{12} & \cdots & P_{1s} \\ P_{21} & P_{22} & \cdots & P_{2s} \\ \cdot & \cdot & \cdots & \cdot \\ P_{r1} & P_{r2} & \cdots & P_{rs} \end{bmatrix} \qquad (5\text{-}67)$$

Without loss of generality, we may assume that the elementary reduction is formed by combining the first two columns of **P**. This situation is described in the channel diagram shown in Figure 5-17.

The reduction results in first one less output

instead of

b_1, b_2 we have $b_1 + b_2 \cdots$ which is accomp stead by adding determ channel cascade as shown

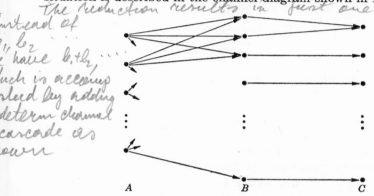

FIGURE 5-17. Channel reduction by cascade.

In Section 5-9 we found necessary and sufficient conditions that a cascade not lose information. These were [(5-61b)]

$$P(a/b) = P(a/c) \qquad (5\text{-}68)$$

for all a, b, and c symbols, such that

$$P(b, c) \neq 0$$

Since we are investigating an elementary reduction, this condition is satisfied trivially for all B symbols except the two symbols we have combined, b_1 and b_2. Let c_1 be the C symbol formed from b_1 and b_2. On applying (5-68) to b_1 and b_2, we find that the necessary and sufficient conditions are

$$P(a/b_1) = P(a/c_1) = P(a/b_2) \qquad \text{for all } a \qquad (5\text{-}69)$$

This is equivalent to†

$$P(a/b_1) = P(a/b_2) \quad \text{for all } a \qquad (5\text{-}70)$$

In other words, *the two output symbols b_1 and b_2 may be combined without loss of information if, and only if, the backward probabilities $P(a/b_1)$ and $P(a/b_2)$ are identical for all a.* This is an important result, both in terms of understanding information and from a practical point of view. It provides conditions under which a channel may be simplified without paying a penalty. The backward probabilities, however, depend upon the a priori probabilities $P(a_i)$; i.e., they depend upon how we use our channel. It is of even more interest to determine when we may combine channel outputs no matter how we use the channel, i.e., for any a priori probabilities. This may be done by using Bayes' law to rewrite (5-70) as

$$\frac{P(b_1/a)P(a)}{\sum_A P(b_1/a)P(a)} = \frac{P(b_2/a)P(a)}{\sum_A P(b_2/a)P(a)} \quad \text{for all } a \qquad (5\text{-}71)$$

or

$$\frac{P(b_1/a)}{P(b_2/a)} = \frac{\sum_A P(b_1/a)P(a)}{\sum_A P(b_2/a)P(a)} \quad \text{for all } a \qquad (5\text{-}72)$$

If (5-72) is to hold for all possible a priori probabilities $P(a)$, we must have

$$P(b_1/a) = \text{const} \times P(b_2/a) \quad \text{for all } a \qquad (5\text{-}73)$$

Equation (5-73) is the condition we seek. If we have a channel matrix satisfying (5-73), we may combine two columns of the matrix, and the new channel matrix will be just as good as the original one. More precisely, for any set of probabilities over the input alphabet, the mutual information of the channel and the reduced channel will be identical. A reduced channel with this property will be called a *sufficient reduction*.

Example 5-10. The channel

$$\begin{bmatrix} \frac{1}{6} & \frac{1}{3} & \frac{1}{2} & 0 \\ \frac{1}{12} & \frac{1}{6} & \frac{1}{4} & \frac{1}{2} \end{bmatrix}$$

may be reduced to

$$\begin{bmatrix} \frac{1}{2} & \frac{1}{2} & 0 \\ \frac{1}{4} & \frac{1}{4} & \frac{1}{2} \end{bmatrix}$$

† The condition on $P(a/c_1)$ follows automatically from (5-70).

and finally to

$$\begin{bmatrix} 1 & 0 \\ \frac{1}{2} & \frac{1}{2} \end{bmatrix}$$

This channel is a sufficient reduction of the original channel.

5-11. Additivity of Mutual Information

Another important property of mutual information is *additivity*. In this section we investigate additivity by considering the average amount of information provided about a set of input symbols by a succession of output symbols. That is, we consider the case where we may gain information about the input by a number of observations, instead of a single observation. An example of this situation occurs when the input symbols of a noisy channel are repeated a number of times, rather than transmitted just once. Such a procedure might be used to improve the reliability of information transmitted through an unreliable channel. Another example is an information channel where the response to a single input is a sequence of output symbols, rather than a single output symbol.

We investigate the additivity property of mutual information in the special case where the output for a single input symbol consists of two symbols. The more general case where the output consists of n symbols may then be treated by induction.

Let us modify our model of the information channel, then, so that instead of a single output for each input, we receive two symbols, say b_j and c_k. The symbols b_j and c_k are from the output alphabets $B = \{b_j\}$, $j = 1, 2, \ldots, s$, and $C = \{c_k\}$, $k = 1, 2, \ldots, t$.

Without loss of generality, we may assume that the two output symbols are received in the order b_j, c_k. Then the a priori probabilities of the input symbols $P(a_i)$ change into the a posteriori probabilities $P(a_i/b_j)$ upon reception of the first output symbol; upon reception of the second output symbol, they change into the "even more a posteriori" probabilities $P(a_i/b_j, c_k)$.

If the two symbols b_j and c_k are received, the average uncertainty or entropy of the set of input symbols changes from

$$H(A) = \sum_A P(a) \log \frac{1}{P(a)} \tag{5-74a}$$

to the a posteriori entropy

$$H(A/b_j) = \sum_A P(a/b_j) \log \frac{1}{P(a/b_j)} \qquad (5\text{-}74b)$$

and then to the "even more a posteriori" entropy

$$H(A/b_j, c_k) = \sum_A P(a/b_j, c_k) \log \frac{1}{P(a/b_j, c_k)} \qquad (5\text{-}74c)$$

As in Section 5-5, we average $H(A/b_j)$ over the b_j to find the average a posteriori entropy, or the equivocation of A with respect to B:

$$\sum_B P(b)H(A/b) = H(A/B) \qquad (5\text{-}75a)$$

In the same manner, we may average $H(A/b_j, c_k)$ over all b_j and c_k in order to find the equivocation of A with respect to B and C:

$$\sum_{B,C} P(b, c)H(A/b, c) = H(A/B, C) \qquad (5\text{-}75b)$$

The results of our generalization of Shannon's first theorem (Section 5-5) apply directly to $H(A/B, C)$; $H(A/B, C)$ is the average number of binits necessary to encode a symbol from the A alphabet after we are given the corresponding B and C symbols.

Equations (5-75a) and (5-75b) suggest two different ways we might measure the amount of information B and C yield about A—the mutual information of (B, C) and A. First, we might define the mutual information of A and (B, C), just as we did when the channel output consisted of a single symbol. That is,

$$I(A; B, C) = H(A) - H(A/B, C) \qquad (5\text{-}76)$$

Second, we might consider the amount of information provided about A by B alone, and then the amount of information about A provided by C *after we have seen B*. These quantities are

$$H(A) - H(A/B) \qquad (5\text{-}77a)$$

and

$$H(A/B) - H(A/B, C) \qquad (5\text{-}77b)$$

The first of these has already been defined as

$$I(A; B) = H(A) - H(A/B) \qquad (5\text{-}78a)$$

It is natural to define (5-77b) as

$$I(A; C/B) = H(A/B) - H(A/B, C) \qquad (5\text{-}78b)$$

called the mutual information of A and C, given B. Upon adding (5-78a) and (5-78b), we find

$$\begin{aligned} I(A; B) + I(A; C/B) &= H(A) - H(A/B, C) \\ &= I(A; B, C) \end{aligned} \qquad (5\text{-}79)$$

Equation (5-79) expresses the additivity property of mutual information. It says that the average information provided by an observation does not depend upon whether we consider the observation in its entirety or broken into its component parts. This equation may be generalized immediately to

$$I(A; B, C, \ldots, D) = I(A; B) + I(A; C/B) + \cdots \\ + I(A; D/B, C, \ldots) \qquad (5\text{-}80)$$

where the term on the left is the average amount of information about A provided by an observation from the alphabets $B, C, \ldots, D$. The first term on the right is the average amount of information about A provided by an observation from the alphabet B. The second term on the right is the average amount of information about A provided by an observation from the alphabet C *after* an observation from the alphabet B, etc.

The particular order of the information we receive is, of course, irrelevant for (5-79) and (5-80). For example, we may write [corresponding to (5-79)]

$$I(A; B, C) = I(A; C) + I(A; B/C) \qquad (5\text{-}81)$$

We may write the information quantities discussed above in several different forms. From (5-76) we have

$$\begin{aligned} I(A; B, C) &= H(A) - H(A/B, C) \\ &= \sum_A P(a) \log \frac{1}{P(a)} - \sum_{A,B,C} P(a, b, c) \log \frac{1}{P(a/b, c)} \\ &= \sum_{A,B,C} P(a, b, c) \log \frac{1}{P(a)} \\ &\qquad - \sum_{A,B,C} P(a, b, c) \log \frac{1}{P(a/b, c)} \\ &= \sum_{A,B,C} P(a, b, c) \log \frac{P(a/b, c)}{P(a)} \qquad (5\text{-}82a) \end{aligned}$$

Another useful form is found by multiplying the numerator and denominator of the logarithm of the above equation by $P(b, c)$.

$$I(A; B, C) = \sum_{A,B,C} P(a, b, c) \log \frac{P(a, b, c)}{P(a)P(b, c)} \qquad (5\text{-}82b)$$

The reader should note the similarity of (5-82a) and (5-82b) to (5-31a) and (5-31b). We might have obtained (5-82a) and (5-82b) merely by replacing b in (5-31a) and (5-31b) by (b, c). This argument suggests the definition

$$H(B, C/A) = \sum_{A,B,C} P(a, b, c) \log \frac{1}{P(b, c/a)} \qquad (5\text{-}83)$$

It is easily verified that

$$I(A; B, C) = H(B, C) - H(B, C/A) \qquad (5\text{-}84)$$

Example 5-11. To illustrate the additivity of mutual information, we examine the BSC

$$\begin{bmatrix} \bar{p} & p \\ p & \bar{p} \end{bmatrix}$$

where $\bar{p} = 1 - p$. This time, however, we assume that the input symbol (either 0 or 1) is repeated, so that the output of the channel consists of two binary symbols b_j, c_k for each input symbol a_i. Furthermore, for simplicity we assume that the two inputs are chosen with equal probabilities. Therefore, setting $\omega = \frac{1}{2}$ in (5-48), we find

$$I(A; B) = 1 - H(p) \qquad (5\text{-}85)$$

To find $I(A; B, C)$, we use (5-82b). Table 5-2 gives the necessary probabilities.

TABLE 5-2. PROBABILITIES OF A REPETITIVE BSC

a_i	b_j	c_k	$P(a_i)$	$P(a_i, b_j, c_k)$	$P(b_j, c_k)$
0	0	0	$\frac{1}{2}$	$\frac{1}{2}\bar{p}^2$	$\frac{1}{2}(p^2 + \bar{p}^2)$
0	0	1	$\frac{1}{2}$	$\frac{1}{2}p\bar{p}$	$p\bar{p}$
0	1	0	$\frac{1}{2}$	$\frac{1}{2}p\bar{p}$	$p\bar{p}$
0	1	1	$\frac{1}{2}$	$\frac{1}{2}p^2$	$\frac{1}{2}(p^2 + \bar{p}^2)$
1	0	0	$\frac{1}{2}$	$\frac{1}{2}p^2$	$\frac{1}{2}(p^2 + \bar{p}^2)$
1	0	1	$\frac{1}{2}$	$\frac{1}{2}p\bar{p}$	$p\bar{p}$
1	1	0	$\frac{1}{2}$	$\frac{1}{2}p\bar{p}$	$p\bar{p}$
1	1	1	$\frac{1}{2}$	$\frac{1}{2}\bar{p}^2$	$\frac{1}{2}(p^2 + \bar{p}^2)$

Using these probabilities in (5-82b) yields

$$I(A \, ; \, B, \, C) = p^2 \log \frac{2p^2}{p^2 + \bar{p}^2} + \bar{p}^2 \log \frac{2\bar{p}^2}{p^2 + \bar{p}^2}$$

$$= (p^2 + \bar{p}^2) \left[1 - H \left(\frac{p^2}{p^2 + \bar{p}^2} \right) \right] \qquad (5\text{-}86)$$

The interpretation of (5-86) is clear.   If we observe the outputs 10 or 01 from such a channel, its meaning is entirely ambiguous; the two possible inputs will still be equally probable, and we gain no information from our observation. If, on the other hand, we observe 00 or 11, we gain information about the input equivalent to that gained by observing a single output from a BSC with error probability

$$\frac{p^2}{p^2 + \bar{p}^2}$$

From (5-85) the information of such an observation is

$$1 - H \left(\frac{p^2}{p^2 + \bar{p}^2} \right) \qquad (5\text{-}87)$$

We observe either 00 or 11 with probability $p^2 + \bar{p}^2$; hence (5-86).

The arguments given above are easily generalized to the case of a BSC used with more than a single repetition.   For example, if each input produces three binary outputs, we obtain

$$I(A \, ; \, B, \, C, \, D) = (p^3 + \bar{p}^3) \left[1 - H \left(\frac{p^3}{p^3 + \bar{p}^3} \right) \right] + 3p\bar{p}[1 - H(p)] \quad (5\text{-}88)$$

Equations (5-85), (5-86), and (5-88) are plotted in Figure 5-18.

5-12. Mutual Information of Several Alphabets

In our investigation of the additivity of mutual information in Section 5-11, we were led to a consideration of the sequence of entropy quantities.

$$\begin{aligned} &H(A) \\ &H(A/B) \\ &H(A/B, \, C) \\ &\qquad . \\ &\qquad . \\ &\qquad . \end{aligned} \qquad (5\text{-}89)$$

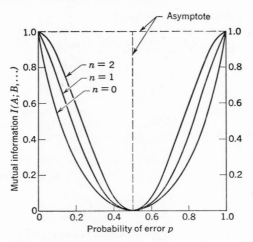

FIGURE 5-18. Mutual information of a BSC with n repetitions.

Each member of this sequence is no greater than the preceding member. We saw that the difference between two successive members could be interpreted as the average information about A provided by a new observation.

$$I(A; B) = H(A) - H(A/B) \qquad (5\text{-}90a)$$
$$I(A; C/B) = H(A/B) - H(A/B, C) \qquad (5\text{-}90b)$$

$\cdots \cdots \cdots \cdots \cdots \cdots \cdots \cdots$

$I(A; B)$ is the mutual information of A and B; $I(A; C/B)$ is the mutual information of A and C after we are given B. Both these quantities, however, involve the mutual information of just two alphabets. It is also possible to define the mutual information of more than two alphabets (McGill, 1954). We define the mutual information of A, B, and C by

$$I(A; B; C) = I(A; B) - I(A; B/C) \qquad (5\text{-}91a)$$

Our definition of the mutual information of A, B, and C implies that $I(A; B; C)$ is symmetric in A, B, and C. If this is true,

(5-91a) can also be written

$$I(A;B;C) = I(B;C) - I(B;C/A) \qquad (5\text{-}91b)$$
$$= I(C;A) - I(C;A/B) \qquad (5\text{-}91c)$$

To prove the symmetry of $I(A;B;C)$, we write (5-91a) as

$$I(A;B;C) = \sum_{A,B} P(a,b) \log \frac{P(a,b)}{P(a)P(b)}$$
$$- \sum_{A,B,C} P(a,b,c) \log \frac{P(a,b/c)}{P(a/c)P(b/c)}$$
$$= \sum_{A,B,C} P(a,b,c) \log \frac{P(a,b)P(a/c)P(b/c)}{P(a)P(b)P(a,b/c)}$$
$$= \sum_{A,B,C} P(a,b,c) \log \frac{P(a,b)P(a,c)P(b,c)}{P(a)P(b)P(c)P(a,b,c)}$$
$$= H(A) + H(B) + H(C) - H(A,B) - H(A,C)$$
$$- H(B,C) + H(A,B,C) \qquad (5\text{-}92)$$

In addition to exhibiting the symmetry we want, (5-92) is reminiscent of the expression for the mutual information of two alphabets:

$$I(A;B) = H(A) + H(B) - H(A,B) \qquad (5\text{-}93)$$

It is easy to generalize (5-92) and (5-93) to more than three alphabets. For example, the mutual information of A, B, C, and D is

$$I(A;B;C;D) = I(A;B;C) - I(A;B;C/D)$$
$$= [H(A) + H(B) + H(C) + H(D)]$$
$$- [H(A,B) + H(A,C) + H(A,D) + H(B,C)$$
$$+ H(B,D) + H(C,D)] + [H(A,B,C)$$
$$+ H(A,B,D) + H(A,C,D) + H(B,C,D)]$$
$$- [H(A,B,C,D)] \qquad (5\text{-}94)$$

Blachman (1961) has suggested a generalization of Figure 5-9 to aid in the interpretation of the above expressions. For three alphabets, we have the relationships shown in Figure 5-19.

Although Figure 5-19 is an important aid in remembering relationships among the quantities we have defined, it can also be somewhat deceptive. The mutual information $I(A; B)$ was shown to be nonnegative; the mutual information $I(A; B; C)$, however,

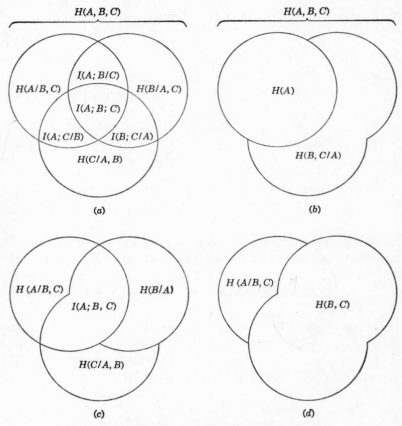

FIGURE 5-19. Some information relationships.

can be negative. This means that the intersection of the three circles of Figure 5-19a can be *negative!* To show this we present an example.

Example 5-12. Consider the three binary alphabets A, B, C. Let a_i and b_j be selected as 0 or 1, each with probability $\frac{1}{2}$ and each independently of the other. Finally, we assume that c_k is selected as 0 if a_i equals b_j and as 1 if does not equal b_j. Some of the probabilities of these three random variables are given in Table 5-3.

TABLE 5-3. PROBABILITIES OF THREE RANDOM VARIABLES

$a_i b_j c_k$	$P(a_i, b_j, c_k)$	$P(a_i/b_j, c_k)$	$P(a_i, b_j/c_k)$	$P(a_i, b_j)$	$P(a_i)$
000	$\frac{1}{4}$	1	$\frac{1}{2}$	$\frac{1}{4}$	$\frac{1}{2}$
001	0	0	0	$\frac{1}{4}$	$\frac{1}{2}$
010	0	0	0	$\frac{1}{4}$	$\frac{1}{2}$
011	$\frac{1}{4}$	1	$\frac{1}{2}$	$\frac{1}{4}$	$\frac{1}{2}$
100	0	0	0	$\frac{1}{4}$	$\frac{1}{2}$
101	$\frac{1}{4}$	1	$\frac{1}{2}$	$\frac{1}{4}$	$\frac{1}{2}$
110	$\frac{1}{4}$	1	$\frac{1}{2}$	$\frac{1}{4}$	$\frac{1}{2}$
111	0	0	0	$\frac{1}{4}$	$\frac{1}{2}$

[handwritten margin notes: $P(a_i) = P(b_j) = P(a_i/c_k) = P(b_j/c_k)$]

Using this table, we calculate

$$I(A; B) = 0 \text{ bits}$$
$$I(A; B/C) = 1 \text{ bit}$$
$$I(A; B; C) = I(A; B) - I(A; B/C) = -1 \text{ bit}$$

It is clear why we get such an answer. Since A and B are statistically independent, $I(A; B) = 0$, and B provides no information about A. If we already know C, however, learning B tells us which A was chosen, and therefore provides us with one bit of information.

5-13. Channel Capacity

Consider an information channel with input alphabet A, output alphabet B, and conditional probabilities $P(b_j/a_i)$. In order to calculate the mutual information

$$I(A; B) = \sum_{A,B} P(a, b) \log \frac{P(a, b)}{P(a)P(b)} \qquad (5\text{-}95)$$

it is necessary to know the input symbol probabilities $P(a_i)$. The mutual information, therefore, depends not only upon the channel, but also upon how we use the channel—i.e., the probabilities with which we choose the channel inputs. It is of some interest to examine the variation of $I(A; B)$ as we change the input probabilities.

Example 5-13. For the BSC with probability of error p, we found [(5-48)]

$$I(A; B) = H(\omega p + \bar{\omega}\bar{p}) - H(p) \qquad (5\text{-}96)$$

where ω is the probability of selecting a 0 at the input and $\bar{\omega} = 1 - \omega$, $\bar{p} = 1 - p$. We may plot (5-96) as a function of ω for a fixed p (see Figure 5-20).

Hence, the mutual information of a BSC varies from 0 to $1 - H(p)$. The minimum value of 0 is achieved when $\omega = 0$ or 1. In these cases, the input is known with probability 1 at the output, even before an output symbol is received. The maximum value of $1 - H(p)$ is achieved when $\omega = \frac{1}{2}$, that is, when both inputs are equally probable. *of course then the source A contains a max. of info where if $\omega = 0$ or 1 A contains no info to begin with for the channel to give up or leak.*

this figure plotted from fig. 5-10 p by pt.

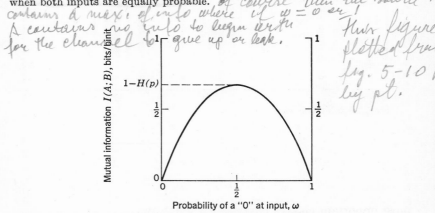

FIGURE 5-20. Mutual information of a BSC.

For a general information channel, we see that the mutual information can always be made 0 by choosing one of the input symbols with probability 1. Since the mutual information is non-negative, this is an easy answer to the question of what is the minimum value of $I(A; B)$. The question of the maximum value of $I(A; B)$ for a general channel is not so easily answered, however. The maximum value of $I(A; B)$ as we vary the input symbol probabilities is called C, the *capacity* of the channel:

$$C = \max_{P(a_i)} I(A; B) \qquad (5\text{-}97)$$

Note that the capacity of an information channel is a function only of the conditional probabilities defining that channel. It does not depend upon the input probabilities—how we use the channel.

at a certain value of a_i $I(A; B)$ is max. this $I(A; B)$ max is the capacity. Now how is C is at this fixed set of a_i's depend o the P b/a_i values & not on the a_i's which are

From Figure 5-20 we see that the capacity of a BSC with error probability p is $1 - H(p)$.

The calculation of the capacity of an information channel is, in general, quite involved (Muroga, 1953; Shannon, 1957b; Fano, 1961). In certain cases, however, the calculation can be simplified. The

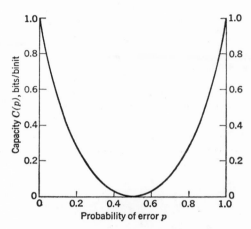

FIGURE 5-21. Capacity of a BSC.

most important class of channels for which the calculation simplifies is the class of *uniform* channels.

Definition. Consider a channel defined by the channel matrix

$$\begin{bmatrix} P_{11} & P_{12} & \cdots & P_{1s} \\ P_{21} & P_{22} & \cdots & P_{2s} \\ \cdot & \cdot & \cdots & \cdot \\ P_{r1} & P_{r2} & \cdots & P_{rs} \end{bmatrix}$$

As before, $P_{ij} = P(b_j/a_i)$. This channel is said to be *uniform* if the terms in every row and every column of the channel matrix consist of an arbitrary permutation of the terms in the first row.

Example 5-14. We have already dealt with one example of a uniform information channel—the BSC. The natural generalization of the BSC, the r-ary symmetric channel (rSC), is a uniform channel with r input and r output symbols. The channel matrix of the rSC is shown in Figure 5-22.

$$\begin{bmatrix} \bar{p} & \dfrac{p}{r-1} & \dfrac{p}{r-1} & \cdots & \dfrac{p}{r-1} \\ \dfrac{p}{r-1} & \bar{p} & \dfrac{p}{r-1} & \cdots & \dfrac{p}{r-1} \\ \cdots & \cdots & \cdots & \cdots & \cdots \\ \dfrac{p}{r-1} & \dfrac{p}{r-1} & \dfrac{p}{r-1} & \cdots & \bar{p} \end{bmatrix}$$

FIGURE 5-22. Channel matrix of the rSC.

As usual, $\bar{p} = 1 - p$. The overall probability of error for this channel is p, but there are $r - 1$ possible incorrect output symbols for each input symbol.

We now calculate the capacity of a general uniform channel. The capacity is the maximum of $I(A; B)$ as we vary the input distribution.

$$\begin{aligned} I(A; B) &= H(B) - H(B/A) \\ &= H(B) - \sum_A P(a) \sum_B P(b/a) \log \frac{1}{P(b/a)} \end{aligned} \quad (5\text{-}98)$$

The summation over B in the last term of (5-98) is a summation, for each a_i, of the terms in the ith row of the channel matrix. For a uniform channel, however, this summation is independent of i. Hence,

$$I(A; B) = H(B) - \sum_B P(b/a) \log \frac{1}{P(b/a)} \quad (5\text{-}99)$$

and the last term of (5-99) is independent of the input symbol distribution. To find the maximum of the right side of (5-99), we need only find the maximum of $H(B)$. Since the output alphabet consists of r symbols, we know that $H(B)$ cannot exceed $\log r$ bits. $H(B)$ will equal $\log r$ bits if and only if all the output symbols occur with equal probability. In general, it is not true that there exists a distribution over the input symbols such that the output symbols are equiprobable. For a uniform channel, however, it is easy to check that equiprobable symbols at the input produce equiprobable symbols at the output. Therefore, the maximum value of (5-99), the capacity of the uniform channel, is

and $P(a/b)$ matrix also has rows made up of the same terms. Hence we also have

$$\max I(A; B) = H(A) - H(A/B) = \log r - \sum_A P(a/b) \log \frac{1}{P(a)}$$

$$C = \log r - \sum_B P(b/a) \log \frac{1}{P(b/a)}$$
$$= \log r + \sum_B P(b/a) \log P(b/a) \tag{5-100}$$

Example 5-15. Using (5-100), we calculate the capacity of the rSC:

$$C = \log r + \bar{p} \log \bar{p} + p \log \frac{p}{r-1}$$
$$= \log r - p \log (r-1) - H(p) \tag{5-101}$$

5-14. Conditional Mutual Information

The channel capacity is the maximum value of

$$I(A;B) = \sum_{A,B} P(a,b) \log \frac{P(b/a)}{P(b)} \tag{5-102}$$

the average of $\log [P(b/a)/P(b)]$ over both the input alphabet A and the output alphabet B. The mutual information may also be written

$$I(A;B) = \sum_A P(a) \sum_B P(b/a) \log \frac{P(b/a)}{P(b)}$$
$$= \sum_A P(a) I(a;B) \tag{5-103}$$

where we have defined

$$I(a;B) = \sum_B P(b/a) \log \frac{P(b/a)}{P(b)} \tag{5-104}$$

$I(a;B)$ is called the *conditional mutual information* (conditional on a). The conditional mutual information is the average of $\log [P(b/a)/P(b)]$ with respect to the conditional probability $P(b/a)$.

In general, $I(a;B)$ depends on the input symbol a. When the input symbols are selected according to a set of probabilities which achieve channel capacity, however, we shall show that $I(a;B)$ does *not* depend upon a for any input symbol with $P(a) \neq 0$. *When the input probabilities are selected so as to achieve capacity,*

$$I(a;B) = C \tag{5-105}$$

for all a such that $P(a) \neq 0$.

This fact is central to the calculation of the channel capacity for channels more general than the uniform channel treated in the previous section (Fano, 1961). We shall use this fact when we prove Shannon's second theorem in Section 6-10.

We prove (5-105) by contradiction. That is, we assume we have a set of input probabilities† $P(a_1)$, $P(a_2)$, . . . , $P(a_r)$ which achieve channel capacity, but for which (5-105) does not hold, and all the $I(a; B)$ are not equal to the capacity. Since the average of $I(a; B)$ does equal the capacity, there must be at least one $I(a; B)$ greater than C and at least one $I(a; B)$ less than C. Without loss of generality, we assume

$$I(a_1; B) > C \qquad (5\text{-}106a)$$
$$I(a_2; B) < C \qquad (5\text{-}106b)$$

Now we change the probabilities

$$P(a_1), P(a_2), P(a_3), \ldots, P(a_r) \qquad (5\text{-}107a)$$

to

$$P(a_1) + \Delta, P(a_2) - \Delta, P(a_3), \ldots, P(a_r) \qquad (5\text{-}107b)$$

where Δ is some small positive number less than $P(a_2)$, and show that the value of the mutual information increases. Since the original probabilities (5-107a) were assumed to achieve capacity, this is a contradiction; hence, our assumption that all the $I(a; B)$ were not constant must have been in error.

Let us denote the new probabilities in (5-107b) by $P_1(a_1)$, $P_1(a_2)$, . . . , $P_1(a_r)$. The corresponding output probabilities will be written $P_1(b_1)$, $P_1(b_2)$, . . . , $P_1(b_s)$. The $P_1(b)$ are given by

$$P_1(b) = \sum_A P_1(a)P(b/a)$$
$$= P(b) + \Delta[P(b/a_1) - P(b/a_2)] \qquad (5\text{-}108)$$

Let $I_1(A; B)$ be the value of the mutual information calculated using the probabilities $P_1(a)$; by assumption, the value of the mutual information using the original probabilities $P(a)$ is C, the channel capacity. We calculate

† We assume that none of the $P(a_i)$ are equal to zero. If $P(a_i) = 0$ we may consider a new channel derived from the old channel by deleting the input a_i.

$$I_1(A; B) - C = \sum_A P_1(a) \sum_B P(b/a) \log \frac{P(b/a)}{P_1(b)}$$

$$- \sum_A P(a) \sum_B P(b/a) \log \frac{P(b/a)}{P(b)}$$

$$= \Delta \left[\sum_B P(b/a_1) \log P(b/a_1) - \sum_B P(b/a_2) \right.$$

$$\left. \times \log P(b/a_2) \right] + \sum_B P_1(b) \log \frac{1}{P_1(b)}$$

$$- \sum_B P(b) \log \frac{1}{P(b)} \quad (5\text{-}109)$$

for each term in the pos. $\sum_A$ there is a term in the negative sum except $P(a_1) + \Delta$ to $P(a_2) - \Delta$ causing residue

Upon adding and subtracting

$$\Delta \left[\sum_B P(b/a_1) \log \frac{1}{P(b)} - \sum_B P(b/a_2) \log \frac{1}{P(b)} \right] \quad (5\text{-}110)$$

on both sides of (5-109), we obtain

$$I_1(A; B) - C = \Delta \left[\sum_B P(b/a_1) \log \frac{P(b/a_1)}{P(b)} \right.$$

$$\left. - \sum_B P(b/a_2) \log \frac{P(b/a_2)}{P(b)} \right] + \sum_B P_1(b) \log \frac{P(b)}{P_1(b)}$$

$$= \Delta \left[I(a_1; B) - I(a_2; B) \right]$$

$$+ \sum_B P_1(b) \log \frac{P(b)}{P_1(b)} \quad (5\text{-}111)$$

with the aid of (5-108) which transforms the last term of (5-109) into one $\sum_B P(b_1) \cdot$ from $\sum_B P(b) \cdots$

We wish to show that the right side of (5-111) is positive, in order to arrive at a contradiction. The first term on the right of (5-111) is positive by (5-106). The second term, however, must be *negative* by our often used inequality (2-8a). Hence, superficially, it appears as if we cannot draw any conclusions about the sign of the right side of (5-111). Such pessimism is not warranted, however, as we shall now demonstrate by examining the last term of (5-111) in more detail. *To show that the neg. term is smaller than the pos.*

$$\sum_B P_1(b) \log \frac{P(b)}{P_1(b)} = \sum_B \left\{ P(b) + \Delta[P(b/a_1) - P(b/a_2)] \right\}$$

$$\times \log \frac{1}{1 + \dfrac{\Delta[P(b/a_1) - P(b/a_2)]}{P(b)}} \quad (5\text{-}112)$$

For x small enough, we may approximate $\log[1/(1+x)]$ by $-x/\ln 2$. Using this fact in (5-112), we see that for Δ sufficiently small

$$\sum_B P_1(b) \log \frac{P(b)}{P_1(b)} \approx \frac{-1}{\ln 2} \sum_B \{P(b) + \Delta[P(b/a_1) - P(b/a_2)]\}$$
$$\times \frac{\Delta[P(b/a_1) - P(b/a_2)]}{P(b)}$$
$$\approx \frac{-\Delta}{\ln 2} \sum_B [P(b/a_1) - P(b/a_2)]$$
$$\frac{-\Delta^2}{\ln 2} \sum_B \frac{[P(b/a_1) - P(b/a_2)]^2}{P(b)}$$
$$\approx \frac{-\Delta^2}{\ln 2} \sum_B \frac{[P(b/a_1) - P(b/a_2)]^2}{P(b)} \tag{5-113}$$

since $\sum_B P(b/a_1) = \sum_B P(b/a_2) = 1$. Thus, the second term (a

negative quantity) of (5-111) goes as Δ^2 for Δ sufficiently small, whereas the first term (a positive quantity) goes as Δ; by making Δ sufficiently small, the right side can be made positive, and we have our contradiction.

The assumption that not all the conditional mutual informations $I(a; B)$ equal the capacity must be incorrect, and we have proved (5-105).

NOTES

Note 1.   We may define a more general zero-memory channel than the channel with a finite number of inputs and outputs defined in Section 5-1.   A zero-memory channel consists of a space of inputs A, a space of outputs B, and a probability measure $p(\cdot/a)$ on B for each a in A.

Therefore information channels are mathematically equivalent to "statistical experiments" (Kempthorne, 1952).   The "hypotheses" of the experiment correspond to channel input symbols, and the "outcomes" of the experiment correspond to channel output symbols.   The structure of an experiment (as well as that of a channel) is then described by a set of conditional probability measures on the "outcome" space.

Many of the questions of interest with respect to general statistical experiments are not important in the case of information channels, and vice versa. One area where both fields have an overlapping interest is in the comparison of experiments, or comparison of information channels (Blackwell, 1953; Lindley, 1956; Shannon, 1958).   As the reader may have inferred, capacity is not the only method of rating the performance of an information channel.   When the number of hypotheses (input symbols) is 2, a large number of concrete results in the statistical literature may be applied (Kullback, 1959; Grettenberg, 1962; Birnbaum, 1961).   In certain cases the traditional statistical methods when applied to information channels lead to results diametrically opposed to those of information theory (Abramson, 1960).

Note 2.   The capacity of human beings playing the role of information channels has been investigated by Pierce and Karlin (1957). ˙They measure the human information capacity by means of a number of reading experiments and conclude:

The discrepancy between human channel capacity measured thus (40–50 bits/second) and telephone and television channel capacity (about 50,000 bits/second and 50,000,000 bits/second respectively) is provocative.

It should be noted that Pierce and Karlin attempt to measure the information comprehended by their subjects; that is, they study the information received at an interior point of the human information processing system.   Kelly (1962), on the other hand, has measured the information capacity of a single human retina and obtained the figure of 10^9 bits per sec.

Note 3.   In the testing of two statistical hypotheses the likelihood ratio (and often the logarithm of the likelihood ratio) plays a central role.   If x and $1 - x$ are the probabilities of hypotheses 1 and 2, respectively, the logarithm of the likelihood ratio is

$$\log \frac{x}{1 - x}$$

Golomb (1961) has used the fact that

$$\int_x^y \log \frac{u}{1 - u} \, du = H(y) - H(x)$$

[where $H(\cdot)$ is the entropy function] to identify the logarithm of the likelihood ratio as an *information density*.   For if the a priori probabilities of the two hypotheses are x and $1 - x$ and if the a posteriori probabilities after the ith experiment outcome (or output symbol) are y_i and $1 - y_i$,

$$\int_x^{y_i} \log \frac{u}{1 - u} \, du = H(y_i) - H(x)$$

which, in the notation of Section 5-4, is $H(A/b_j) - H(A)$.   This difference may be averaged over all possible outcomes to obtain a quantity corresponding to the negative of the mutual information between the experiment outcomes and the hypotheses.

Golomb also generalizes this idea for the case of n rather than just two hypotheses.

Note 4. Shannon (1956) has pointed out that one may construct an algebra of channels. The sum of two channels corresponds to the case where either of the channels (but not both) is used. The input and output alphabets of the new channel are the unions of the original input and output alphabets (see Problem 5-15). The product of two channels corresponds to the case where both channels are used simultaneously. Both the addition and multiplication operations are associative and commutative, and the product distributes over a sum.

Note 5. Kelly (1956) has investigated an alternative interpretation of channel capacity which is of interest in certain economic problems (Murphy, 1962). Consider a gambler observing the output of a BSC with error probability $p < \frac{1}{2}$ and using the observations in order to place bets on the transmitted symbols. If the gambler is interested in maximizing his expected capital after n bets, he should bet all his capital after each observation. Unfortunately, for large n, if he uses this strategy, the gambler will go bankrupt with probability 1. But if the gambler bets some fixed proportion (less than 1) of his capital after each observation, his capital will grow exponentially with the number of bets. Kelly suggests a strategy to maximize the rate of growth of capital (i.e., interest rate) and finds that the maximum value of the rate of growth is C, the channel capacity. A number of generalizations of this problem are also investigated in Kelly's paper.

Note 6. The mutual information of two random variables, $I(A; B)$, need not be defined only for the case where A and B are the input and output alphabets of a channel. As mentioned in this chapter, a_i and b_j can be any two random variables and $I(A; B)$ still provides a measure of the amount of information one gives about the other. Pinsker (1954), Powers (1956), and Gel'fand and Yaglom (1957) have defined the amount of information about a random function contained in another such function—a natural generalization of the mutual information defined in this chapter. Let μ_{ab} be the probability measure of the random variable (a, b), and let μ_a and μ_b be the measures of a and b. If μ_{ab} is absolutely continuous with respect to $\mu_a\mu_b$, Gel'fand and Yaglom's definition is equivalent to

$$I(A; B) = \int_{A,B} \left(\log \frac{d\mu_{ab}}{d\mu_a \, d\mu_b} \right) d\mu_{ab}$$

where $d\mu_{ab}/d\mu_a \, d\mu_b$ is the Radon-Nikodym derivative of μ_{ab} with respect to $\mu_a\mu_b$. If the random variables a and b assume only a finite number of values, this definition reduces to the one given in this chapter. If a and b possess joint and individual probability densities $p(a, b)$, $p(a)$, and $p(b)$,

$$I(A; B) = \iint p(a, b) \log \frac{p(a, b)}{p(a)p(b)} \, da \, db$$

When a and b are jointly gaussian vectors, this reduces to

$$I(A; B) = \tfrac{1}{2} \log \frac{|K_a| \, |K_b|}{|K_{ab}|}$$

where $|K_{ab}|$, $|K_a|$, and $|K_b|$ are the determinants of the covariance matrices of (a, b), a, and b, respectively. If a represents a sample function of a gaussian random process defined on some (possibly infinite) interval and b is some other random variable,

$$I(A; B) = -\tfrac{1}{2} \log \sigma_b^2$$

where σ_b^2 is the normalized mean-square error in estimating b from the observation of a. Finally, when a and b are both sample functions of gaussian random processes defined over the infinite interval, the average rate at which one of these random processes provides information about the other is

$$i(A; B) = \tfrac{1}{2} \int \log \frac{S_a(f)S_b(f)}{S_a(f)S_b(f) - |S_{ab}(f)|^2} \, df$$

where $S_a(f)$ and $S_b(f)$ are the spectral densities of the a and b random processes and $S_{ab}(f)$ is the cross spectral density.

PROBLEMS

5-1. The channel matrix of a binary information channel is

$$\begin{array}{cc} & \begin{array}{cc} b_1 & b_2 \end{array} \\ \begin{array}{c} a_1 \\ a_2 \end{array} & \begin{bmatrix} 0.8 & 0.2 \\ 0.3 & 0.7 \end{bmatrix} \end{array}$$

The symbols corresponding to the rows and columns of this matrix are given for convenience. Let $P(a_1) = P_1$, $P(a_2) = P_2$, $P(b_1) = Q_1$, and $P(b_2) = Q_2$.

(a) Write Equations (5-6) for this channel, expressing the Q_i in terms of the P_i.

(b) Solve these equations for the P_i in terms of the Q_i.

(c) Find $P(a_i/b_j)$ and Q_j for this channel when $P_1 = P_2 = 0.5$.

(d) Express the P_i in terms of the Q_j for this channel, using the $P(a_i/b_j)$ obtained in part c. Compare your answers in parts b and d.

5-2. Each time an input symbol is transmitted over channel 1 it is repeated over channel 2 (see Figure P 5-2), so that the output may be considered to be a

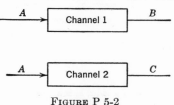

FIGURE P 5-2

pair of symbols (b_j, c_k). Furthermore we assume that the repetition is performed independently of the results of the original transmission, so that

$$P(c_k/a_i, b_j) = P(c_k/a_i)$$

Note that this does *not* mean c_k and b_j are statistically independent.

$$P(c_k/b_j) \neq P(c_k)$$

(*a*) Show that

$$I(A; B, C) = I(A; B) + I(A; C) - I(B; C)$$

Are info gained about source A by observing one output symbol b & one

and provide an interpretation. *put symbol C = similarly said.*

(*b*) Generalize part *a* to the case of *n* channels.

5-3. Use the results of Problem 5-2*a* to check Equation (5-86).

5-4. Prove Equation (5-32):

$$I(A^n; B^n) = nI(A; B)$$

5-5. Consider the information channel shown in Figure P 5-5. For any

$$A = \begin{cases} a_1 \\ a_2 \\ . \\ . \\ . \\ a_r \end{cases} \rightarrow \boxed{} \begin{cases} b_1 \\ b_2 \\ . \\ . \\ . \\ b_s \end{cases} = B$$

FIGURE P 5-5

two sets of input probabilities P_i, $i = 1, 2, \ldots, r$, and Q_i, $i = 1, 2, \ldots, r$, and any λ in [0, 1], the set of numbers $R_i = \lambda P_i + \bar{\lambda}Q_i$ also defines a set of input probabilities, since

$$R_i \geq 0 \qquad \text{for all } i$$

and

$$\sum_{i=1}^{r} R_i = 1$$

Let $I_P(A; B)$, $I_Q(A; B)$, and $I_R(A; B)$ be the mutual information of the above channel when the input probabilities are P_i, Q_i, and R_i.

(*a*) Prove the "convexity" of mutual information. That is, show that

$$I_R(A; B) \geq \lambda I_P(A; B) + \bar{\lambda}I_Q(A; B)$$

(*b*) Show that

$$I_R(A; B) \leq \lambda I_P(A; B) + \bar{\lambda}I_Q(A; B) + H(\lambda)$$

5-6. Generalize parts *a* and *b* of Problem 5-5 to the case where the set of probabilities R_i is formed from *n* sets of probabilities, rather than just 2.

5-7. Consider two information channels with input alphabets A_1 and A_2 and output alphabets B_1 and B_2, respectively (Figure P 5-7). The channel probabilities are $P_1(b/a)$ for channel 1 and $P_2(b/a)$ for channel 2. Let $P_1(a)$ and $P_2(a)$ be the input distributions on A_1 and A_2.

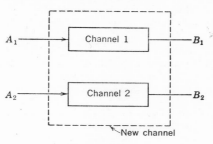

FIGURE P 5-7

(a) Define a new channel with input alphabet A comprised of the symbols of A_1 plus the symbols of A_2. Let the new output alphabet B be comprised of the symbols of B_1 plus the symbols of B_2. An input to the new channel is selected by first choosing either A_1 (with probability λ) or A_2 (with probability $1 - \lambda = \bar{\lambda}$) and then selecting a symbol from that alphabet according to $P_1(a)$ or $P_2(a)$. Express $H(A)$ in terms of $H(A_1)$, $H(A_2)$, and λ.

(b) The channel probabilities of the new channel $P(b/a)$ are given by $P_1(b/a)$ if a and b are in A_1 and B_1, by $P_2(b/a)$ if a and b are in A_2 and B_2, and are equal to zero if a is in A_1 and b in B_2, or a is in A_2 and b in B_1. Find $H(A/B)$ in terms of $H(A_1/B_1)$, $H(A_2/B_2)$, and λ.

(c) Find $I(A, B)$ in terms of $I(A_1; B_1)$, $I(A_2; B_2)$, and λ.

5-8. Generalize Problem 5-7 to the case of n information channels, rather than just 2.

5-9. The *binary multiplicative channel* shown in the sketch has two binary inputs and one binary output. $b = ac$. This channel may be described as an

FIGURE P 5-9

ordinary zero-memory channel by considering the four possible input combinations to comprise a new input alphabet A':

$$A' = \begin{Bmatrix} 00 \\ 01 \\ 10 \\ 11 \end{Bmatrix}$$

(a) Write the channel matrix for the channel with input A' and output B.

(b) The input symbols a and c are selected independently. $\Pr\{a = 0\} = \omega_1$, and $\Pr\{c = 0\} = \omega_2$. Define $1 - \omega_1 = \bar{\omega}_1$ and $1 - \omega_2 = \bar{\omega}_2$. Find $I(A'; B)$. Give an interpretation of your answer.

(c) Find the maximum value of $I(A'; B)$ as ω_1 and ω_2 vary. Find all possible combinations of ω_1 and ω_2 which achieve this maximum value.

5-10. Let **P** be the channel matrix of a channel with r inputs and s outputs. Let a be the number of columns in the matrix having all their elements equal to zero.

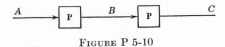

FIGURE P 5-10

(a) If the channel is deterministic, find its capacity.

(b) If (*instead* of the assumption of part a) we assume that the channel is noiseless, find its capacity.

(c) Now make the assumptions of *both* parts a and b at the same time. Two such channels (with the assumptions of parts a and b applying to each) are cascaded, as shown in the sketch. Find the capacity of the cascade channel with input A and output C.

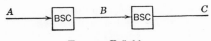

FIGURE P 5-11

5-11. Two BSCs, each with probability of error p, are cascaded, as shown in the sketch. The inputs 0 and 1 of A are chosen with equal probability. Find the following:

(a) $H(A)$.

(b) $H(B)$.

(c) $H(C)$.

(d) $H(A, B)$.

(e) $H(B, C)$.

(f) $H(A, C)$.

(g) $H(A, B, C)$.

(h) $I(A; B; C)$.

5-12. Let a and b be independent identically distributed binary random variables with the probability of a 0 equal to the probability of a 1. Define the binary random variable

$$c = ab$$

(a) Find $H(A)$, $H(B)$, $H(C)$.

(b) Find $I(A; B)$, $I(A; C)$, $I(B; C)$.

(c) Find $H(A, B)$, $H(A, C)$, $H(B, C)$.

(d) Find $H(A, B, C)$.

(e) Find $H(A/B)$, $H(A/C)$, $H(B/C)$.

(f) Find $H(A/B, C)$, $H(B/A, C)$, $H(C/A, B)$.

(g) Find $I(A; B/C)$, $I(B; A/C)$, $I(C; A/B)$.

(h) Find $I(A; B; C)$.

5-13. Let a and b be independent identically distributed binary random variables with the probability of a 0 equal to the probability of a 1. Define the binary random variable $c = a + b$, modulo 2. That is, c is 0 if $a = b$ and c is 1 if $a \neq b$.

(a) Find $H(A)$, $H(B)$, $H(C)$.

(b) Find $I(A; B)$, $I(A; C)$, $I(B; C)$.

(c) Find $H(A, B)$, $H(A, C)$, $H(B, C)$.

(d) Find $H(A, B, C)$.

(e) Find $H(A/B)$, $H(A/C)$, $H(B/C)$.

(f) Find $H(A/B, C)$, $H(B/A, C)$, $H(C/A, B)$.

(g) Find $I(A; B/C)$, $I(B; A/C)$, $I(C; A/B)$.

(h) Find $I(A; B; C)$.

5-14. Find the capacity of

$$\begin{bmatrix} 1 - p - q & q & p \\ p & q & 1 - p - q \end{bmatrix}$$

The special case of $p = 0$ is called the *binary erasure channel*. Provide an interpretation of the capacity of the binary erasure channel.

5-15. Let P_1 and P_2 be the channel matrices of two channels with input alphabets A_1 and A_2 and output alphabets B_1 and B_2, respectively. Form a new channel matrix $\mathbf{P}$ with input alphabet $A = A_1 \cup A_2$ and output alphabet $B = B_1 \cup B_2$, as shown below:

$$\mathbf{P} = \begin{bmatrix} \mathbf{P}_1 & \mathbf{O} \\ \mathbf{O} & \mathbf{P}_2 \end{bmatrix}$$

$\mathbf{O}$ represents a matrix with all zero elements.

Let $P(a_i)$ be the probability of an input symbol $a_i \in A$. Let $Q_1 = \sum_{A_1} P(a_i)$ and $Q_2 = \sum_{A_2} P(a_i)$. Q_i is just the probability that a symbol from A_i is sent. Let C_1, C_2, and C be the capacities of P_1, P_2, and P, respectively.

(a) Find the values of Q_i (in terms of C_1 and C_2) which achieve capacity for the channel $\mathbf{P}$.

(b) Find C in terms of C_1 and C_2.

(c) Extend the results of (a) and (b) to cover the case where n, instead of just 2, channels are combined.

5-16. (a) Find the capacity of the channel

$$\begin{bmatrix} \bar{p} & p & 0 & 0 \\ p & \bar{p} & 0 & 0 \\ 0 & 0 & \bar{p} & p \\ 0 & 0 & p & \bar{p} \end{bmatrix}$$

Sketch the capacity as a function of p.

(b) Find the capacity of

$$\begin{bmatrix} 1 & 0 & 0 \\ 0 & p & p \\ 0 & p & p \end{bmatrix}$$

Sketch the capacity as a function of p and compare with your answer to part a.

5-17. Find the capacity of the following two channels:

(a)

$$\begin{pmatrix} p - \epsilon & p - \epsilon & 2\epsilon \\ p - \epsilon & p - \epsilon & 2\epsilon \end{pmatrix}$$

(b)

$$\begin{pmatrix} p - \epsilon & p - \epsilon & 2\epsilon & 0 \\ p - \epsilon & p - \epsilon & 0 & 2\epsilon \end{pmatrix}$$

(c) Use the approximation

$$\log (1 + \epsilon) \approx \frac{\epsilon}{\ln 2} \qquad \text{for } \epsilon \approx 0$$

to find and compare the behavior of the above two channels for small ϵ.

6

RELIABLE MESSAGES THROUGH UNRELIABLE CHANNELS

6-1. Introduction

In Chapter 6 we shall prove Shannon's second theorem—the most surprising as well as the most important single result of information theory. Because of the significance of this theorem, it would be well to stand back and survey the main results we have already obtained. We have been able to justify our use of entropy and entropy-derived measures of information in two instances—Shannon's first theorem (Section 4-3) and the generalization of this theorem dealing with equivocation (Section 5-5). Shannon's first theorem

147

provided us with a yardstick with which to measure the information emerging from a source.   Using this theorem, we were able to rate symbols from a source in terms of an equivalent number of binits (or r-ary symbols) necessary to represent these symbols.   The generalization of this theorem showed that we could use a quantity related to entropy (equivocation) as a yardstick to measure the results of transmitting information through a channel.

In order to encode symbols from a source alphabet A, we know that we must provide, on the average, $H(A)$ binits per source symbol.   If the symbols from A are transmitted through a channel, however, and we are allowed to observe the output symbols from alphabet B, we need only $H(A/B)$ binits per A symbol in order to represent these input symbols.   Hence, the reception of the channel outputs has provided us with $H(A) - H(A/B)$ binits in the sense just described.   The equivocation $H(A/B)$ can vary from $H(A)$ (when the channel input and output are statistically independent) to zero (when the channel is noiseless).   As it does, the number of binits per A symbol that we receive varies from zero to $H(A)$.

Transmitting $H(A) - H(A/B)$ binits of information is an achievement of some importance.   Still, the form in which these binits appear at the output of our information channel leaves much to be desired.   Let us examine this point in greater detail.   Assume that we transmit a block of n symbols from a source A over an information channel.   Then, if our channel is noiseless, $H(A/B)$ is zero, and each output symbol contains $H(A)$ bits of information; we may reconstruct the sequence of n channel inputs from the sequence of n channel outputs, and it is clear that we have received $H(A)$ bits of *error-free* information.   If our channel is not noiseless, however, the equivocation will not, in general, be zero, and each output symbol will contain only $H(A) - H(A/B)$ bits of information.   Furthermore, note the crucial way in which this information differs from the information out of a noiseless channel.   We cannot reconstruct the channel input sequence perfectly from a knowledge of the channel output sequence.   All we can say is that we can encode the channel inputs, using $H(A) - H(A/B)$ fewer binits per symbol if we know the outputs.   Hence, although we get information through the channel, we do not have *error-free* knowledge of the message transmitted.   This is the fly in the ointment, which we shall remove by Shannon's second theorem.

$H(A) - H(A/B) = I(A;B)$ is the *info* that the channel transmitted about the source symbols, or made known

Shannon's second theorem was first published in 1948.   The birth of information theory may be dated from Shannon's publication of this fundamental paper.   Nevertheless, Shannon's original proof of this theorem contained certain difficulties (McMillan, 1953). The first rigorous proof of Shannon's second theorem was presented by Feinstein in 1955.   Subsequently, different proofs were provided by Shannon (1957a); Blackwell, Breiman, and Thomasian (1959); and Fano (1961).   The proof presented in this chapter is somewhat simpler than any of the proofs mentioned above.

6-2. Error Probability and Decision Rules

Shannon's second theorem deals with the amount of error-free information we can get through a channel.   In order to appreciate more fully the significance of this theorem, let us look into the question of the error probability of a channel.   For some of the simple channels we have used—such as the BSC and the rSC—it is intuitively clear what it is reasonable to call the error probability of the channel.   Nevertheless, we shall see that, even in these cases, the error probability will depend upon a factor not yet considered in our study of information channels.   For example, consider the BSC

$$\begin{bmatrix} 0.9 & 0.1 \\ 0.1 & 0.9 \end{bmatrix} \tag{6-1}$$

Ordinarily we would say that the probability of error of this channel is 0.1.   Note, however, that this statement depends upon the assumption that the channel is used in a "reasonable" manner. If the receiver were to examine the channel output and decide that a *one* was sent when a *zero* is received and vice versa, the probability of error would be 0.9.   Of course, this is not a reasonable way to use such a channel, but it is a possibility we must consider.   The error probability depends upon how the receiver interprets the output symbols of the channel.

To bring out this point in a more meaningful case, take the channel

$$\begin{bmatrix} 0.5 & 0.3 & 0.2 \\ 0.2 & 0.3 & 0.5 \\ 0.3 & 0.3 & 0.4 \end{bmatrix} \tag{6-2}$$

This channel has three inputs a_1, a_2, a_3 and three outputs, b_1, b_2, b_3. When a particular channel output is received, which input should we say was sent? This question prompts the following definition.

> *Definition.* Consider a channel with an r-symbol input alphabet $A = \{a_i\}$, $i = 1, 2, \ldots, r$, and an s-symbol output alphabet $B = \{b_j\}, j = 1, 2, \ldots, s$. A decision rule, $d(b_j)$, is any function specifying a unique input symbol for each output symbol.

Example 6-1. Two possible decision rules for the channel of (6-2) are

$$d(b_1) = a_1$$
$$d(b_2) = a_2 \qquad\qquad (6\text{-}3)$$
$$d(b_3) = a_3$$

one decision rule

and

$$d(b_1) = a_1$$
$$d(b_2) = a_2 \qquad\qquad (6\text{-}4)$$
$$d(b_3) = a_2$$

For a channel with r inputs and s outputs, there are r^s different possible decision rules. The question which prompted our definition of a decision rule may, therefore, be rephrased as "Which one of these r^s decision rules should we use?" The answer to this question will depend upon what we are trying to accomplish, but a reasonable goal for our purposes is the minimization of the error probability of the channel. Hence, we seek a decision rule which minimizes the error probability of our channel. To find such a rule, we calculate the probability of error P_E. This probability may be written as the average of $P(E/b_j)$, the conditional probability of error given that the output of the channel is b_j.

$$P_E = \sum_B P(E/b)P(b) \qquad\qquad (6\text{-}5)$$

Equation (6-5) expresses the error probability as a sum of non-negative terms. Therefore, in order to minimize P_E by choice of a decision rule $d(b_j)$, we may select $d(b_j)$ to minimize each term in the sum separately. $P(b_j)$ does not depend upon the decision rule we use; so it is equivalent to choose $d(b_j)$ to minimize the conditional probability of error $P(E/b_j)$.

For a *fixed* decision rule, $d(b_j) = a_i$,

$$P(E/b_j) = 1 - P[d(b_j)/b_j] \qquad\qquad (6\text{-}6)$$

$P(E/b_j) + P[d(b_j)/b_j] = 1$, *says that probab... an error in transmitting b_j plus the prob... of not having an error in the same case must =*

where, since our decision rule is fixed, $P[d(b_j)/b_j]$ is the backward probability $P(a_i/b_j)$. Finally, in order to minimize (6-6) for each b_j, we choose

$$d(b_j) = a^* \tag{6-7a}$$

where a^* is defined by

$$P(a^*/b_j) \geq P(a_i/b_j) \qquad \text{for all } i \tag{6-7b}$$

In other words, *the channel error probability is minimized if we use that decision rule which chooses for each output symbol the input symbol with the highest probability.* This decision rule is sometimes called a *conditional maximum-likelihood* decision rule. The conditional maximum-likelihood decision rule depends upon the a priori probabilities $P(a_i)$. We may use Bayes' law to write (6-7b) as

$$\frac{P(b_j/a^*)P(a^*)}{P(b_j)} \geq \frac{P(b_j/a_i)P(a_i)}{P(b_j)} \qquad \text{for all } i \tag{6-8}$$

Hence, when the a priori probabilities are all equal, the conditional maximum-likelihood decision rule may be written

$$d(b_j) = a^* \tag{6-9a}$$

where

$$P(b_j/a^*) \geq P(b_j/a_i) \qquad \text{for all } i \tag{6-9b}$$

The decision rule defined by (6-9b) is known as the *maximum-likelihood* decision rule. The maximum-likelihood decision rule does not depend upon the a priori probabilities. When the a priori probabilities are all equal, the maximum-likelihood decision rule results in a minimum value for the probability of error. Even if the a priori probabilities are not equal, however (or even if these probabilities are unknown), we may still employ this decision procedure; in such cases, of course, we are not assured of obtaining a minimum value of the channel error probability.

Example 6-2. From (6-9) we may immediately write a maximum-likelihood decision rule for the channel of (6-2). Such a rule is

$$d(b_1) = a_1$$
$$d(b_2) = a_3$$
$$d(b_3) = a_2$$

Note that this rule is not unique. There are, in fact, three maximum-likelihood decision rules for this channel.

The error probability using any given decision rule is easily obtained with the aid of (6-5) and (6-6).

$$P_E = \sum_B P(E/b)P(b)$$
$$= \sum_B P(b) - \sum_B P[d(b)/b]P(b)$$
$$= 1 - \underbrace{\sum_B P[d(b), b]}_{\bar{P}_E} \tag{6-10}$$

The terms in the summation of (6-10) are just the joint probabilities that $d(b_j) = a^*$ is transmitted and b_j is received (for each j). Hence, defining $\bar{P}_E = 1 - P_E$, we may rewrite (6-10) as

$$(error\ free\ h)\quad \bar{P}_E = \sum_B P(a^*, b) \tag{6-11}$$

Since

$$\sum_{A,B} P(a, b) = 1 \tag{6-12}$$

we may also rewrite (6-10) as

$$P_E = \sum_{B, A-a^*} P(a, b) \tag{6-13}$$

The notation $\sum_{A-a^*}$ is meant to indicate a sum over all members of the A alphabet except $d(b_j) = a^*$. An alternative way of writing (6-13) is

$$P_E = \sum_{B, A-a^*} P(b/a)P(a) \tag{6-14}$$

If the a priori probabilities $P(a)$ are all equal, then (6-14) becomes

$$P_E = \frac{1}{r} \sum_{B, A-a^*} P(b/a) \tag{6-15}$$

Equation (6-15) is of some interest since (for the special case of equal a priori probabilities) it provides an expression for the channel error probability in terms of a sum over the elements of the channel matrix $P(b/a)$. The sum is over all elements of the channel matrix, except that one term [corresponding to $d(b_j)$] is omitted from each column.

$$\bar{P}_E = \sum_B P(b/a^*) \cdot P(a^*) = \frac{1}{r} \sum_B P(b/a^*)$$

Example 6-3. We calculate the error probability of the channel used in Examples 6-1 and 6-2.

$$\begin{bmatrix} 0.5 & 0.3 & 0.2 \\ 0.2 & 0.3 & 0.5 \\ 0.3 & 0.3 & 0.4 \end{bmatrix} \tag{6-16}$$

We assume that all three input symbols are chosen with equal probabilities and that a maximum-likelihood decision rule is used. (Recall that this rule results in a minimum P_E for equal a priori probabilities.)

$$P_E = \tfrac{1}{3}[(0.2 + 0.3) + (0.3 + 0.3) + (0.2 + 0.4)]$$
$$= 0.567$$

6-3. The Fano Bound

The error probability has been presented in the previous section without reference to entropy, equivocation, or mutual information. The purpose of Chapter 6 is to show a connection between these two separate sets of ideas. As a first step in this direction, we provide upper and lower bounds on the equivocation in terms of the error probability.

In what follows we shall make repeated use of (6-11) and (6-13).

$$\bar{P}_E = \sum_B P(a^*, b) \tag{6-11}$$

$$P_E = \sum_{B, A-a^*} P(a, b) \tag{6-13}$$

Using these two relationships, we construct the identity

$$H(P_E) + P_E \log (r - 1) = P_E \log \frac{r-1}{P_E} + \bar{P}_E \log \frac{1}{\bar{P}_E}$$
$$= \sum_{B, A-a^*} P(a, b) \log \frac{r-1}{P_E}$$
$$+ \sum_B P(a^*, b) \log \frac{1}{\bar{P}_E} \tag{6-17}$$

The equivocation $H(A/B)$ may be written in terms of the same sort of summations:

$$H(A/B) = \sum_{B, A-a^*} P(a, b) \log \frac{1}{P(a/b)}$$
$$+ \sum_B P(a^*, b) \log \frac{1}{P(a^*/b)} \tag{6-18}$$

Subtracting (6-17) from (6-18) yields

$H(A/B) - H(P_E) - P_E \log (r - 1)$

$$= \sum_{B,A-a^*} P(a, b) \log \frac{P_E}{(r - 1)P(a/b)}$$
$$+ \sum_B P(a^*, b) \log \frac{\bar{P}_E}{P(a^*/b)} \quad (6\text{-}19)$$

Now we employ (2-2) to change the base of the logarithms in the right side of (6-19),

$(\log e)^{-1}[H(A/B) - H(P_E) - P_E \log (r - 1)]$

$$= \sum_{B,A-a^*} P(a, b) \ln \frac{P_E}{(r - 1)P(a/b)}$$
$$+ \sum_B P(a^*, b) \ln \frac{\bar{P}_E}{P(a^*/b)} \quad (6\text{-}20)$$

so that we may use the inequality

$$\ln x \leq x - 1 \quad (6\text{-}21)$$

on each term in the summations. The right side of (6-20) is less than or equal to

$$\sum_{B,A-a^*} P(a, b)\left[\frac{P_E}{(r - 1)P(a/b)} - 1\right] + \sum_B P(a^*, b)\left[\frac{\bar{P}_E}{P(a^*/b)} - 1\right]$$
$$= \left[\frac{P_E}{r - 1} \sum_{B,A-a^*} P(b)\right] - P_E + \left[\bar{P}_E \sum_B P(b)\right] - \bar{P}_E$$
$$= 0 \quad (6\text{-}22)$$

and we have the inequality we seek,

$$H(A/B) \leq H(P_E) + P_E \log (r - 1) \quad (6\text{-}23)$$

This important inequality was first derived by Fano. It is valid, no matter what decision rule we use, although the error probability can depend drastically upon the decision rule. The form of this inequality suggests an interesting interpretation. Assume that we have some fixed decision rule. When we receive an output symbol, we need $H(P_E)$ bits of information to specify whether our decision rule has produced an error. It produces an error with probability P_E, and then we may specify which of the remaining

$r - 1$ input symbols was sent with at most log $(r - 1)$ bits. The above interpretation, unfortunately, is not adequate as a proof of (6-23), although it may be used as the basis of a proof somewhat different from the one we have used.

Let us examine the condition for equality in the Fano bound (6-23). The inequality

$$\ln x \leq x - 1 \qquad (6\text{-}21)$$

becomes an equality if and only if $x = 1$. Using this condition in (6-23), we find that the Fano bound becomes an equality if and only if

$$P(a/b) = \frac{P_E}{r - 1} \qquad \text{for all } b \text{ and } a \neq a^* \qquad (6\text{-}24a)$$

if all $P(a/b)$ are equal then all $P(a)$ must be equal

and

$$P(a^*/b) = \bar{P}_E \qquad \text{for all } b \qquad (6\text{-}24b)$$

Since

$$\sum_A P(a/b) = 1 \qquad \text{for all } b$$

the second condition, (6-24b), follows from the first, (6-24a). Equation (6-24a) implies, for each b, that all input symbols except the one selected by our decision rule are equally probable. This condition thus serves to reinforce our interpretation of the Fano bound. *Also, 6-24 b implies that all the probabilities of the decision rule for each b are equal*

6-4. Reliable Messages and Unreliable Channels

The object of Shannon's second theorem is to describe the fundamental limitations on the transmission of reliable error-free messages through an unreliable channel. Consider first the use of a BSC to transmit reliable messages (Figure 6-1).

$$A = \left\{ \begin{matrix} 0 \\ 1 \end{matrix} \right. \rightarrow \boxed{\text{BSC}} - \left. \begin{matrix} 0 \\ 1 \end{matrix} \right\} = B$$

FIGURE 6-1. A BSC.

To be even more specific, we assume that p, the probability of error of this BSC, is 0.01. Thus, 99 per cent of the binits transmitted are received correctly. For many modern data-transmission systems, however, this level of reliability is far from adequate.

Probability of error requirements of 10^{-6}, 10^{-8}, or even lower are often necessary. In order to increase the reliability of our channel we may have to repeat our message several times. For example, suppose we decide to send each message (0 or 1) *three* times. One method of viewing this procedure is illustrated in Figure 6-2.

Unused signals	Messages	Outputs
	000	000
001		001
010		010
011		011
100	→(BSC)³—	100
101		101
110		110
	111	111

FIGURE 6-2. A method of increasing reliability.

The output of the channel under these circumstances is an element of $(BSC)^3$—a binary sequence of length 3. The probability that no errors occur in the transmission of our three digits is

$$(1-p)\cdot(1-p)(1-p) = (1 - p)^3 = (\bar{p})^3$$

[handwritten: prob. of right in first dig 2nd, 3rd]

The probability of just one error is *[handwritten: 3 X error in one digit. no err in 2nd no error in 3rd]* $= 3p\bar{p}^2$ *[handwritten: $p\cdot\bar{p}^2 + p\bar{p}^2 + p\bar{p}^2$]*

The probability of two errors is *[handwritten: (and one right)]*

$$p^2\bar{p} + p^2\bar{p} + p^2\bar{p} = 3p^2\bar{p}$$

while the probability that all three binits will be received in error is

$$p^3$$

Whenever p is less than $\frac{1}{2}$ (i.e., whenever the probability that a binit is received correctly is greater than the probability that it is received incorrectly), it seems reasonable to decide that the message was 000 or 111, according to the majority vote of the three received binits. This decision rule need not be justified on purely democratic grounds; it is easy to see that this is the maximum-likelihood decision rule. In any event, such a decision rule leads to a probability of interpreting the message in error† P_E (equal to the sum of the probabilities of three binit errors and two binit errors) of

$$P_E = p^3 + 3p^2\bar{p} \qquad (6\text{-}25)$$

For $p = 0.01$, this yields

$$P_E \approx 3 \times 10^{-4} \qquad (6\text{-}26)$$

Thus we have been able to reduce the probability of error from a value of 10^{-2} (when sending 0 or 1) to a value of 3×10^{-4} (when sending 000 or 111). Having gone this far, it is not difficult to see how to increase the reliability even further. We may send *five* binits over the channel for each binary message we wish to transmit. This is represented in Figure 6-3.

Unused signals	Messages	Outputs
	00000	00000
00001		00001
00010		00010
00011		00011
.	→ (BSC)⁵ ⟶	.
.		.
.		
11110		
	11111	11111

FIGURE 6-3. A method of increasing reliability.

The probability of zero, one, two, three, four, or five binit errors in transmission is

$$\bar{p}^5$$
$$5p\bar{p}^4$$
$$10p^2\bar{p}^3$$
$$10p^3\bar{p}^2$$
$$5p^4\bar{p}$$
$$p^5$$

† The probability of message error will ordinarily depend upon the a priori message probabilities. Because of the symmetry in the situation we are describing, however, the error probability is independent of the a priori probabilities.

respectively. If we again use a majority rule (i.e., maximum likelihood) to decide whether 00000 or 11111 was transmitted, we obtain a probability of error

$$P_E = p^5 + 5p^4\bar{p} + 10p^3\bar{p}^2 \qquad (6\text{-}27)$$

(i.e., the sum of the probabilities of five, four, or three binit errors). For $p = 0.01$, this yields

$$P_E \approx 10^{-5} \qquad (6\text{-}28)$$

There is, of course, no limit to this crude method of increasing reliability. In Table 6-1 we give the probability of message error when 1, 3, 5, 7, 9, and 11 binits per message are used in a BSC with single-binit probability of error of $p = 0.01$.

TABLE 6-1. PROBABILITY OF MESSAGE ERROR IN A BSC

Binits per binary message	Probability of message error
1	10^{-2}
3	3×10^{-4}
5	10^{-5}
7	4×10^{-7}
9	10^{-8}
11	5×10^{-10}

The improvement displayed in Table 6-1 is not achieved without penalty. The price we pay for increased message reliability is increased redundancy in the transmitted binits. In other words, although we may decrease the probability of error from 10^{-2} to 5×10^{-10} by going from 1 binit per binary message to 11 binits per binary message, we must also decrease the message rate from 1 message per binit to $\frac{1}{11}$ message per binit. In general, the simple repetitive method we have described can lead to *an exchange of message rate for message reliability*. Typically such an exchange will appear as plotted in Figure 6-4.

6-5. An Example of Coding to Correct Errors

An important question is suggested by Figure 6-4. The coding scheme that we have investigated so far—simple repetition—is the most obvious method of exchanging rate for reliability.   Do there exist more sophisticated and more efficient methods of making this exchange?   That is, for a given value of probability of message error in Figure 6-4, do there exist coding methods which give us a greater message rate than that achieved by simple repetition?   The answer to this question is an emphatic "Yes!"

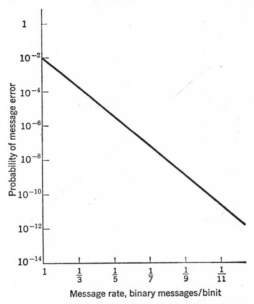

FIGURE 6-4. Exchange of rate for reliability in a BSC using repetition.

The answer to this question is provided by Shannon's second theorem (Section 6-10).   It not only states that we can do better than is indicated in Figure 6-4, but it also tells us *how much* better we can do.   Indeed the "how much better" answer provided by Shannon's theorem is the most amazing part of the story we have to tell.   We have sketched this answer in Figure 6-5.

Shannon's second theorem tells us that for *any* message rate less than the channel capacity C, we can find codes such that the probability that a message will be in error is less than *any* positive number ϵ—i.e., as small as we want it.   The theorem presents us with the unexpected result that it is *not* necessary to require the message rate to approach 0 in order to achieve more and more reliable operation of the channel.

In Section 6-4 we discussed the possibility of achieving virtually error-free information transmission through an unreliable channel— the BSC. Let us now investigate the exchange of message rate for reliability a little more carefully. In the previous section we decreased our rate by simply repeating the binary message we

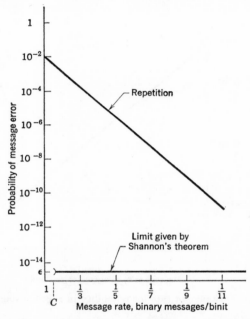

FIGURE 6-5. Two possible exchanges of rate for reliability in a BSC.

wished to transmit. As indicated in Figures 6-1 and 6-2, this can be viewed as increasing the order of the channel extension we use and selecting only two of the possible extension input symbols, α_i, as messages. A more powerful method of varying the message rate—the method we shall employ in proving Shannon's second theorem—is to fix the order of the extension we use but to vary the number of channel input symbols, α_i, used as messages. Again we illustrate this for the case of the BSC in Figure 6-6.

Suppose we can transmit binary symbols through a BSC at the rate of one per second. Then the α_i, consisting of sequences of

3 binits, can be transmitted at the rate of one every 3 sec. If we select only the two sequences 000 and 111 as allowable messages, as shown in the previous section, we can obtain a probability of error

$$P_E = 3 \times 10^{-4} \tag{6-29}$$

while the message rate is $\frac{1}{3}$ binit per sec. If, on the other hand, we use all eight of the α_i as messages, the probability that a message

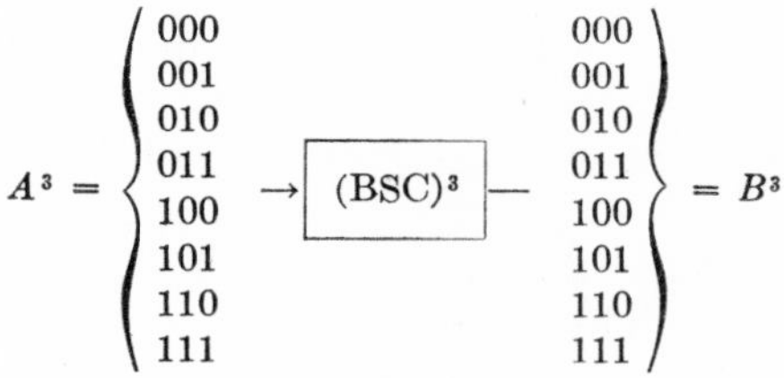

$$A^3 = \begin{Bmatrix} 000 \\ 001 \\ 010 \\ 011 \\ 100 \\ 101 \\ 110 \\ 111 \end{Bmatrix} \rightarrow \boxed{(\text{BSC})^3} \leftarrow \begin{Bmatrix} 000 \\ 001 \\ 010 \\ 011 \\ 100 \\ 101 \\ 110 \\ 111 \end{Bmatrix} = B^3$$

FIGURE 6-6. Third extension of the BSC.

(not a binit) will be transmitted correctly is $\bar{p}^3$. The probability of a message error then is $1 - \bar{p}^3$. For $p = 0.01$, this yields

$$P_E \approx 3 \times 10^{-2} \tag{6-30}$$

The message rate corresponding to this probability of error is 1 binit per sec. There are possibilities between these two extremes, of course. We might select four of the α_i as code words representing four equiprobable messages. For example, let the four messages be represented by

$$\begin{matrix} 000 \\ 011 \\ 101 \\ 110 \end{matrix} \tag{6-31}$$

If these four α_i are chosen, we may use the maximum-likelihood decision rule† shown in Figure 6-7.

† As shown in Example 6-2, the maximum-likelihood rule is not unique. In this example, there are several maximum-likelihood rules, in addition to the one shown in Figure 6-7.

	Outputs	Messages selected
	$\left.\begin{array}{l} 000 \\ 001 \end{array}\right\} \longrightarrow$	000
	$\left.\begin{array}{l} 010 \\ 011 \end{array}\right\} \longrightarrow$	011
	$\left.\begin{array}{l} 100 \\ 101 \end{array}\right\} \longrightarrow$	101
	$\left.\begin{array}{l} 110 \\ 111 \end{array}\right\} \longrightarrow$	110

FIGURE 6-7. A maximum-likelihood decision rule.

Then the probability that a message will be interpreted correctly, $\bar{P}_E$, is just the probability that the first two binits are transmitted without error, or

$$\bar{P}_E = \bar{p}^2 \tag{6-32}$$

For $p = 0.01$, this yields

$$P_E \approx 2 \times 10^{-2} \tag{6-33}$$

Since the *four* binary sequences we use correspond to *two* binary messages and we take 3 sec to transmit each message, the message rate is just $\frac{2}{3}$ binit per sec. Comparing the results of selecting two, four, or eight messages from the eight possible inputs of the (BSC)[3], we see that, in general, *the more messages we use, the higher the probability of a message error.*

The nth extension of a source with r input symbols has a total of r^n input symbols which we may use. If we use only M of these possibilities as messages, however, we may decrease the probability of error. *The trick is to decrease the probability of error without requiring M to be so small that the message rate,† (log M)/n, becomes too small.* Shannon's second theorem tells us that the probability of error can be made *arbitrarily small* as long as M is less than 2^{nC}.

---

† We measure the message rate in equivalent binary messages per symbol. Thus, sending one of M possible messages using n symbols is equivalent to sending log M binary messages in n symbols and a message rate of (log M)/n binary messages per symbol.

For this M, the message rate is

$$\frac{\log M}{n} = C \qquad (6\text{-}34)$$

and the channel capacity is seen to correspond to the upper limit of the *error-free message rate!*

6-6. Hamming Distance

In Sections 6-7 and 6-8 we prove Shannon's second theorem for the special case of the BSC. We can take advantage of the binary nature of the input and output symbols to simplify this theorem for the BSC. Hamming has introduced the useful idea of the distance between two binary sequences (Hamming, 1950). The *hamming distance* between two binary sequences of the same length, α_i and β_j, is defined as the number of places in which α_i and β_j differ. For example, let

$$\alpha_i = 101111$$
$$\beta_j = 111100$$

and let $D(\alpha_i, \beta_j)$ be the hamming distance between α_i and β_j. Then $D(\alpha_i, \beta_j) = 3$.

The concept of hamming distance may be applied to the three different codes for the $(\text{BSC})^3$ discussed in the previous section.

TABLE 6-2. THREE CODES FOR THE $(\text{BSC})^3$

	Code α	Code $\mathcal{B}$	Code $\mathcal{C}$
	000	000	000
	001	011	111
	010	101	
	011	110	
	100		
	101		
	110		
	111		
No. of messages M:	8	4	2

The code words of the three codes given in Table 6-2 may be shown as vertices of three-dimensional cubes. Then the hamming distance between any two code points can be seen to be the number of steps we must take to go from one point to the other. Note that the minimum distances between code points in codes $\mathcal{A}$, $\mathcal{B}$, and $\mathcal{C}$ are 1, 2, and 3, respectively.

The minimum distance between code points of a code is closely related to the probability of error of the code. In general, the greater the minimum distance, the lower the error probability we can expect when using the code. Of course, the greater the minimum distance, the fewer code points we can pack onto the vertices of an n-dimensional cube. This is but another expression of an effect noted in the previous section. The advantages of being able to represent a large number of messages with a code must be weighed

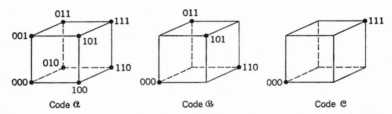

FIGURE 6-8. Three codes for the (BSC)^3.

against the advantages of a low channel error probability when using that code.

Errors arising in the transmission of α_0, a sequence of n binits, over a (BSC)^n will cause the received sequence β_j to differ from the transmitted sequence. If D errors occur during transmission, the hamming distance between α_0 and β_j will be D.

$$D(\alpha_0, \beta_j) = D \qquad (6\text{-}35)$$

The *average* number of errors occurring in a block of n binits will be np, where p is the error probability of the BSC. Thus the average hamming distance between a transmitted and a received sequence is also np. The actual distance between a transmitted and a received sequence, of course, will rarely be equal to this average. Hence, we must look into the problem of determining which code word was transmitted when an output sequence β_j is received from the channel—i.e., which decision rule to use.

Throughout this chapter we may assume that our messages (and hence our code words) are equiprobable. In Section 6-2 we showed that the maximum-likelihood decision rule minimized the error probability when all possible inputs were equiprobable. We now show that the maximum-likelihood decision rule has a simple interpretation in terms of hamming distance. Let α_i be the transmitted code word and β_j be any possible channel output sequence. As before, let the hamming distance between these two binary sequences of length n be D. Then α_i and β_j differ in exactly D places, and the probability that β_j will be received if α_i is sent is just the probability

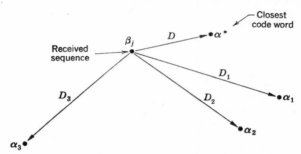

FIGURE 6-9. Maximum-likelihood decision rule for the $(BSC)^n$.

that errors will occur in the D places where they differ and that no errors will occur in the $n - D$ remaining places:

$$P(\beta_j/\alpha_i) = (p)^D (\bar{p})^{n-D} \tag{6-36}$$

For $p < \frac{1}{2}$ (the only case of any interest), $P(\beta_j/\alpha_i)$ decreases with increasing D. The farther β_j is from the transmitted binary sequence, the less likely it is to be received. The maximum-likelihood decision rule selects that code word which maximizes $P(\beta_j/\alpha_i)$; hence, for any received sequence β_j, the maximum-likelihood rule selects the code word closest to β_j in the hamming-distance sense.

6-7. Shannon's Second Theorem for the BSC—The First Step

We now prove Shannon's second theorem for the special case of the BSC. The more general theorem valid for any zero-memory information channel with a finite number of symbols will be proved in Section 6-9.

Shannon's Second Theorem (Special Case)

Consider a BSC with error probability p, and hence capacity $C = 1 - H(p)$. Let ϵ be an arbitrarily small positive number, and let $M = 2^{n(C-\epsilon)}$. Then, for n sufficiently large, it is possible to select a subset of M code words (to represent M equiprobable messages) from the set of 2^n possible inputs to the $(BSC)^n$, such that the probability of error in decoding the channel output can be made as small as we wish.

In Figure 6-10 we have indicated the 2^n possible inputs and 2^n outputs of the nth extension of a BSC with probability of error p.

A^n		B^n
00 · · · 00		00 · · · 00
00 · · · 01	$\rightarrow$ (BSC)^n —	00 · · · 01
00 · · · 10		00 · · · 10
· · · · · · ·		· · · · · · ·
11 · · · 11		11 · · · 11

FIGURE 6-10. The nth extension of a BSC.

The inputs and outputs of this channel consist of sequences of n binary digits. In order to send M messages through this channel, we select M of the 2^n possible inputs as code words. In Section 6-5 we indicated how the probability of message error P_E increases as M increases. The question we must now answer is, "How many messages is it possible to send and still have the message error probability remain small?"

Of course, the answer to this question must depend upon how we select our input symbols for the messages. If we select the code words so that they cluster together, we can expect a higher probability of error than if we construct a code with the same number of code words more or less equally spaced from one another. The method of coding will be crucial to the probability of error we obtain and, therefore, to the maximum number of messages we may use. Let us defer this important question, however, and assume that somehow we have selected a code consisting of M code words of n binits each for use with the $(BSC)^n$.

because then the average difference between code words in number of differing digits will be greatest and hence it will be [hard?] to make a mistake by having just one or two or [...]

When one of these code words, say α_0, is sent through the channel, some other binary sequence of length n, say β_j, is received (Figure 6-11).

$$\alpha_0 \quad \rightarrow \boxed{(BSC)^n} \longleftarrow \quad \beta_j$$

FIGURE 6-11. The channel.

We know that the maximum-likelihood decision rule described in the previous section will minimize our probability of error if all M messages are sent with equal probability. The maximum-likelihood rule is difficult to analyze, however. Accordingly, we shall use another closely related type of decision rule. Although the rule we describe will not be so good as the maximum-likelihood rule, we shall find that we can still attain a probability of error as small as we wish.

We have already noted that the average distance between the transmitted sequence α_0 and the received sequence β_j will be np, where n is the order of the BSC we use (or the block length of the code), and p is the probability of error of the BSC. When we receive a symbol β_j out of our channel, therefore, our natural inclination is to hunt for the transmitted code symbol among those (if any) code symbols at a distance np or less from β_j. In geometrical terms we can say that we draw a sphere of radius np about β_j and hunt for α_0 in this sphere. The quantity np is only the average distance of α_0 from β_j, however, and it might be prudent to enlarge our sphere a bit, as insurance that α_0 will be inside the sphere with high probability.

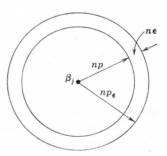

FIGURE 6-12. A sphere about the received symbol.

Mathematicians are wont to call such insurance ϵ, and we follow their time-honored custom. Consider a sphere of radius np_ϵ about β_j, where $p_\epsilon = p + \epsilon$ (Figure 6-12).

Our decision procedure will be to draw the sphere of radius np_ϵ about β_j and, if there is a *unique* code point inside this sphere, we shall decide that such a point was the one transmitted. If there is no unique code point inside the sphere (either because there are none or because there are more than one), we just throw up our hands and make an error! Now the reader may object that, in the latter circumstances, we are giving up too easily. The reader is correct in this objection. Nevertheless, we shall still be able to show that this procedure leads to a negligible probability of error.

Using the procedure just described, there are two ways in which an error in decoding a received symbol may occur. Let $S(np_\epsilon)$ indicate a sphere of radius np_ϵ about the received symbol (Figure 6-13). The first way is if α_0, the transmitted code word, is not in

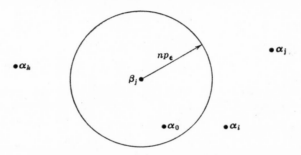

FIGURE 6-13. Correct decoding of β_j.

$S(np_\epsilon)$; the only other way an error can occur is if α_0 is in $S(np_\epsilon)$ but some other code word is also in $S(np_\epsilon)$. Hence we may write the probability of error as

$$P_E = \Pr \{\alpha_0 \not\in S(np_\epsilon)\} + \Pr \{\alpha_0 \in S(np_\epsilon)\}$$
$$\times \Pr \{\text{at least one other code word} \in S(np_\epsilon)\} \quad (6\text{-}37)$$

where $\in$ and $\not\in$ are read "is contained in" and "is not contained in," respectively. Since $\Pr \{\alpha_0 \in S(np_\epsilon)\} \leq 1$, (6-37) implies

$$P_E \leq \Pr \{\alpha_0 \not\in S(np_\epsilon)\}$$
$$+ \Pr \{\text{at least one other code word} \in S(np_\epsilon)\} \quad (6\text{-}38)$$

The probability that at least one of two possible events will occur is never greater than the sum of the individual probabilities that each will occur. A generalization of this law implies

$$\Pr \{\text{at least one other code word} \in S(np_\epsilon)\}$$
$$\leq \sum_{\alpha_i \neq \alpha_0} \Pr \{\alpha_i \in S(np_\epsilon)\} \quad (6\text{-}39)$$

where the summation on the right is over the $M - 1$ code words not transmitted. Substitution of (6-39) into (6-38) gives us the inequality we need:

$$P_E \leq \Pr\{\alpha_0 \notin S(np_\epsilon)\} + \sum_{\alpha_i \neq \alpha_0} \Pr\{\alpha_i \in S(np_\epsilon)\} \quad (6\text{-}40)$$

Equation (6-40) expresses a simple bound on the probability of error for a specific set of M code words. The first term of (6-40) is the probability that the received word and the transmitted word *will not* be within a hamming distance of $n(p + \epsilon)$ from each other; the second term is the sum of probabilities (one for each word not transmitted) that the received word and each word *not* transmitted *will* be within a hamming distance of $n(p + \epsilon)$ from each other.

The first term of (6-40) is easy to evaluate. It is just the probability that more than $n(p + \epsilon)$ errors were made in the transmission of n binits through a BSC with probability of error p. The *average* number of errors occurring in a block of n binits is np. For any finite value of n, there will be some finite probability that the number of errors will exceed its mean value by $n\epsilon$ or more. As n increases, however, this becomes less and less probable; more precisely the weak law of large numbers (Parzen, 1961) tells us that for any two positive numbers ϵ and δ there exists an n_0 such that for any $n > n_0$ the probability that the number of errors exceeds its mean value by more than $n\epsilon$ is less than δ. This means that by taking n large enough we may be sure that

$$\Pr\{\alpha_0 \notin S(np_\epsilon)\} < \delta \quad (6\text{-}41)$$

with δ as small as we wish.

With this equation, half the work in evaluating the error probability (6-40), and thus half the work in proving Shannon's second theorem, is done. Using (6-41) in (6-40) yields

$$P_E \leq \delta + \sum_{\alpha_i \neq \alpha_0} \Pr\{\alpha_i \in S(np_\epsilon)\} \quad (6\text{-}42)$$

Note that δ was independent of the set of M code words we chose to represent our M messages. The last term of (6-42), on the other hand, depends quite strongly on the code we happen to choose. How then can we use (6-42) to provide a bound for the probability of error without going into the difficult question of which code to use?

The answer to this dilemma is provided by an ingenious argument due to Shannon. Instead of evaluating (6-42) for some particular code, Shannon showed that it is possible to evaluate (6-42) averaged over all possible codes. The first term of (6-42) does not depend upon the code we use. The summation of $M - 1$ terms in (6-42) does; if, however, we average the summation over all possible codes we shall obtain the average probability of error—averaged over all possible codes. This is not exactly what we started out to calculate but we shall see that it is enough to prove the fundamental theorem.

6-8. Random Coding—The Second Step

Shannon's argument—sometimes called random coding—proceeds as follows. In order to pick M input code words for our code, we select them at random from the set of 2^n possible channel inputs. We may think of the 2^n input symbols as written on 2^n separate slips of paper and mixed together in a large bowl. We are then blindfolded and told to select M slips from the bowl. After each slip is selected, it is read and replaced in the bowl before the next slip is selected. The M slips of paper then define M code words for us. †

Each time we select a code word there are 2^n possibilities. We make M separate selections; hence, there are a total of 2^{nM} different codes we might end up with. Each of these codes is selected with probability 2^{-nM}. The error probability obtained with any specific code is given in (6-42). We now average (6-42) over our 2^{Mn} possible codes to obtain the average error probability $\bar{P}_E$. We have already noted that δ, the first term on the right side of (6-42), does not depend upon the code we choose. Hence, we need only average $M - 1$ terms of the form $\Pr \{\alpha_i \in S(np_e)\}$, where $\alpha_i \neq \alpha_0$. Using a wavy bar to indicate an averaging over the 2^{Mn} different

---

† The coding procedure described may result in a singular code—that is, we may select the same slip of paper more than once, and therefore use the same code word for more than one message. For $M \ll 2^n$, such an occurrence is unlikely but possible. For $M > 2^n$ such an occurrence is inevitable.

$\sum_{i \neq 0}$ has $M-1$ terms. for 2^{Mn} codes we take the ave over each of the $M-1$ terms. Because of the randomness of each code of 2^{Mn} codes, each of the $M-1$ ave $\Pr\{\alpha_i \in S np_e\}$ will be equal to the o...

codes, we rewrite (6-42) as

[handwritten marginalia: α_0 in one code may not be the same word as in another code hence all P_E are equal]

$$\widetilde{P_E} \leq \delta + (M - 1)\ \overbrace{\Pr\{\alpha_i \in S(np_\epsilon)\}}$$
$$\leq \delta + M\ \overbrace{\Pr\{\alpha_i \in S(np_\epsilon)\}} \qquad \alpha_i \neq \alpha_0 \qquad (6\text{-}43)$$

To evaluate $\overbrace{\Pr\{\alpha_i \in S(np_\epsilon)\}}$, $\alpha_i \neq \alpha_0$, in (6-43), we make use of the simplicity of the coding procedure used to generate α_i. The α_i were selected from the 2^n possible code words at random; hence the average probability that α_i, a code word not equal to the transmitted code word α_0, is contained in a sphere of radius np_ϵ about the received sequence β_j is equal to the ratio of $N(np_\epsilon)$, the total number of different binary sequences in the sphere, to 2^n, the total number of different binary sequences of length n.

$$\overbrace{\Pr\{\alpha_i \in S(np_\epsilon)\}} = \frac{N(np_\epsilon)}{2^n} \qquad \alpha_i \neq \alpha_0 \qquad (6\text{-}44)$$

Finally, we obtain a bound for $N(np_\epsilon)$. The number of binary sequences of length n at a distance of exactly k from β_j is just the number of possible ways a binary sequence of length n can differ from β_j in exactly k places, or just the binomial coefficient $\binom{n}{k}$. Summing over all values of k less than or equal to np_ϵ, we obtain†

$$N(np_\epsilon) = 1 + \binom{n}{1} + \binom{n}{2} + \cdots + \binom{n}{np_\epsilon}$$
$$= \sum_{k=0}^{np_\epsilon} \binom{n}{k} \qquad (6\text{-}45)$$

We can bound this sum with an often used inequality of information theory (Peterson, 1961, p. 246; Wozencraft and Reiffen, 1961, p. 71):

$$\sum_{k=0}^{np_\epsilon} \binom{n}{k} \leq 2^{nH(p_\epsilon)} \qquad \text{for } p_\epsilon < \tfrac{1}{2} \qquad (6\text{-}46)$$

Hence, on combining (6-44), (6-45), and (6-46), we obtain

$$\overbrace{\Pr\{\alpha_i \in S(np_\epsilon)\}} \leq 2^{-n[1-H(p_\epsilon)]} \qquad \alpha_i \neq \alpha_0 \qquad (6\text{-}47)$$

† Of course, np_ϵ need not be an integer. In this case we must replace np_ϵ in the last binomial coefficient of (6-45) with the largest integer less than np_ϵ. The proof, however, is changed in no respect.

and using this result in (6-43) produces the bound

$$\widetilde{P_E} \leq \delta + M2^{-n[1-H(p_\epsilon)]} \qquad (6\text{-}48)$$

Equation (6-48) contains the essence of Shannon's second theorem (for the special case of the BSC). For the parameter δ can be made as small as we wish by increasing the block length n. Hence, the total right side of (6-48) can be made as small as we want, as long as

$$\log M < n[1 - H(p_\epsilon)] < n[1 - H(p)] \qquad (6\text{-}49)$$

This is the expression we seek. By taking ϵ small,

$$H(p_\epsilon) = H(p + \epsilon)$$

can be made arbitrarily close to $H(p)$, and we may choose a number of messages M as close to $2^{n[1-H(p)]}$ as we want. But $1 - H(p)$ is the capacity C of the BSC. Hence, we may choose M messages, where M is any number less than 2^{nC}, and the average probability of error can be made less than any preassigned value. There must be at least one code which does as well as the average, and so we are assured that there exists a code with $M < 2^{nC}$ code words with error probability arbitrarily small.

This is the result we promised at the end of Section 6-5. If we use a long enough block length n, we may choose any number of code words M up to 2^{nC} for use with a BSC, and still have the probability of misrecognizing a code word as small as we wish. Hence, we may send up to [see (6-34)]

$$\frac{\log M}{n} = \frac{\log 2^{nC}}{n} = C \qquad (6\text{-}50)$$

essentially error-free binary messages with each binit over a BSC of capacity C.

6-9. Shannon's Second Theorem—Discussion

The theorem proved in the last two sections is admittedly of a very special nature. The channel considered is the simplest non-trivial channel—the BSC. Nevertheless, all the important ideas necessary for the proof of the more general theorem and all the important consequences which follow from the more general theorem are illustrated in these sections.   We use the present section to discuss these ideas and implications before proving the general theorem in Section 6-10.

The first idea we discuss is *random coding*, introduced by Shannon. It is necessary to understand what is meant by such a coding procedure if we are to appreciate the limitations of the theorem. Because of the fact that the code words were selected at random, we could use Equation (6-47) to bound the probability that an arbitrary code word would be in the sphere of radius np_ϵ surrounding β_j.   If we had fixed the code words in some deterministic fashion, we would not be able to speak of the probability that a code word is within a distance np_ϵ of the received sequence β_j in this way.   Looking at this matter even more closely, it is possible to view the coding procedure we have described as really no coding procedure at all.

As a practical method of coding or finding a good set of code words, random coding leaves much to be desired.   If we use this procedure, on the average we can make the probability of error as small as we wish.   The average referred to here, unfortunately, is the average over the ensemble of possible codes.   Thus we are not assured, once we arrive at some fixed code, that we have a good code.   As an extreme example, note that it is possible to obtain the highly singular code where all M messages are mapped into the same code word.

Shannon's second theorem can, therefore, be characterized as a little more than an existence proof, but a little less than a constructive proof.   The theorem does not exactly show us how to construct a good code, and so we do not quite have a method of finding codes. On the other hand, the theorem does provide us with a method which will generate good codes *on the average;* so it is not as bad as a pure existence proof.

In the more general version of Shannon's second theorem proved in the next section, we show that we may select $M = 2^{n(C-\epsilon)}$, $\epsilon > 0$, code words (where C is the capacity of the channel) and still have the message error probability as small as we wish.   We shall also prove a partial converse to this theorem: namely, if we choose $M = 2^{n(C+\epsilon)}$, $\epsilon > 0$, code words, it is not possible to find a decision rule resulting in an arbitrarily small probability of error P_E by increasing n, the block length of the code.   This form of the converse will be sufficient for our purposes.   We note, however, that several stronger forms may be proved.   Wolfowitz (1959) has shown that if we choose $M = 2^{n(C+\epsilon)}$ code words (where C is the channel capacity and $\epsilon > 0$), then the best probability of error approaches *one* as n increases!

The coding theorem states that we can make the probability of misinterpreting a word sent through a noisy channel to represent one of our messages as small as we wish, while keeping the message rate of the channel fixed.   The important point of the previous sentence is that the theorem deals with the probability of error of messages, or code *words*.   For example, in the case of the BSC, the theorem says that the probability of misinterpreting a sequence of n zeros and ones is arbitrarily small.   This is much stronger than merely saying that the probability of misinterpreting a single *binit* is arbitrarily small.   This distinction has led to misunderstandings in interpreting the results of the various forms of the converse of Shannon's second theorem.   In terms of the BSC treated in the previous section, the converse states that if the number of equiprobable messages M is greater than 2^{nC} (where again C is the capacity of the BSC), the probability of error in a word approaches 1 as n increases.   This conclusion will hold for any set of code words (not just on the average with respect to an ensemble of codes) and for any decision rule.   The theorem is of great mathematical interest, but its relevance to the communication problem is often overemphasized.   The theorem does not state that effective communication is impossible if $M > 2^{nC}$.   To clarify this point, let us plot the probability of a *binit* error in a BSC versus the message rate when the binits are chosen to be 0 or 1 with equal probability.

For any message rate, R binary messages per binit, less than C, the capacity of the channel, we know that the probability of a binit error can also be made as small as we wish.   For a message rate R greater than C, we can think of the following procedure. We again employ the nth extension of the BSC to transmit messages and let n increase.   To achieve a message rate of R binary messages per binit, we must have 2^{nR} messages to send through the nth extension of the BSC.   Alternatively, we may send nR binits through the nth extension.   We can send just under nC of these binits through the channel with arbitrarily small probability of error.   For the remaining $nR - nC$ binits we must transmit, we shall require the receiver to decide on 0s or 1s by merely flipping a coin—heads for a 0, tails for a 1.   For *these* binits the probability of error will be $\frac{1}{2}$.   The probability of binit error averaged over both the reliable and unreliable binits will be slightly greater than $\frac{1}{2}(R - C)/R$.   This result is portrayed in Figure 6-14.

That part of Figure 6-14 which gives the probability of error for $R > C$ is obtained by use of the procedure we have outlined.   We have not shown that this procedure is the best possible procedure,

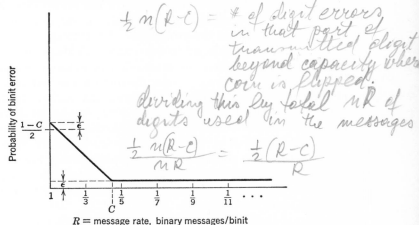

$$\frac{1}{2} n(R-C) = \text{\# of digit errors in that part of transmitted digit beyond capacity when coin is flipped.}$$

$$\text{dividing this by total } nR \text{ of digits used in the messages}$$

$$\frac{1}{2} n(R-C)}{nR} = \frac{1}{2}(R-C)}{R}$$

FIGURE 6-14. Binit error rate in the BSC as a function of message rate.

however.   In fact, the calculation of the smallest possible *binit* error probability for message rates $R > C$ is still an open question. In addition, note that although we have terminated the abscissa in Figure 6-14 at $R = 1$, we can obtain even higher message rates by using the coin-tossing procedure we have described.   For example, consider a noiseless BSC ($p = 0$).   Then our coin-tossing procedure leads to a probability of binit error of 0.25 at a message rate of 2 binary messages per binit.

A final point to be discussed before we turn to a general proof of Shannon's second theorem is that of probability of error bounds. In both the proof for the BSC and the general proof, we are interested only in demonstrating that the probability of error can be made arbitrarily small when $M \leq 2^{n(C-\epsilon)}$.   A large number of results,

$$\frac{1}{2}(R-C)$$
$$\frac{1}{2}\left(\frac{R}{2-1}\right)$$
$$= \frac{1}{4} = .25$$

however, have been obtained, detailing exactly how fast the probability of error can be made to approach 0 as n, the order of the extension used, is increased. We do not treat this subject other than to remark that many authors have been able to obtain exponential (or almost exponential) behavior of the probability of error with n. Some of these results are referenced in the notes at the end of this chapter.

6-10. Shannon's Second Theorem—General Case

Let us now turn to a proof of Shannon's second theorem for the general discrete channel without memory. In concept, the proof will be remarkably similar to the proof presented for the BSC in Sections 6-7 and 6-8.

Shannon's Second Theorem

Consider a channel with r inputs, s outputs, and channel capacity C. Let ϵ be an arbitrarily small number, and let $M = 2^{n(C-\epsilon)}$. Then, for n sufficiently large, it is possible to select a subset of M code words (to represent M equiprobable messages) from the set of r^n possible inputs to the nth extension of the channel, such that the probability of error in decoding the channel output can be made as small as we wish.

In Figure 6-15 we have indicated the r^n possible inputs and the s^n outputs of the nth extension of our channel.

A^n	B^n
$\alpha_1 = (a_1 \cdots a_1 a_1)$	$\beta_1 = (b_1 \cdots b_1 b_1)$
$\alpha_2 = (a_1 \cdots a_1 a_2) \rightarrow \boxed{(\text{channel})^n} \leftarrow$	$\beta_2 = (b_1 \cdots b_1 b_2)$
$\cdots \cdots \cdots \cdots \cdots$	$\cdots \cdots \cdots \cdots$
$\alpha_{r^n} = (a_r \cdots a_r a_r)$	$\beta_{s^n} = (b_s \cdots b_s b_s)$

FIGURE 6-15. The nth extension of a channel.

In order to send M messages through this channel we select M of the r^n possible inputs as code words. Again we ask the question, "How many messages is it possible to send and still have the message error probability remain small?"

When a code word, say α_0, is sent through the channel, some output, say β_j, is received (Figure 6-16).

$$\alpha_0 \;\rightarrow\; \boxed{(\text{channel})^n} \;\leftarrow\; \beta_j$$

FIGURE 6-16. The channel.

Since all M messages are assumed equiprobable, the decision rule minimizing the probability of error is the maximum-likelihood rule

$$d(\beta_j) = \alpha^* \tag{6-51a}$$

where
$$P(\beta_j/\alpha^*) \geq P(\beta_j/\alpha_i) \qquad \text{for all } i \tag{6-51b}$$

Again we shall find it convenient to calculate the error probability, using a decision rule closely related to the maximum-likelihood rule rather than the maximum-likelihood rule itself. We want to write a condition defining α^* equivalent to (6-51b). Since the logarithm is a monotonic function, we can replace (6-51b) by

$$\log P(\beta_j/\alpha^*) \geq \log P(\beta_j/\alpha_i) \qquad \text{for all } i \tag{6-52a}$$

or

$$\log \frac{1}{P(\beta_j/\alpha^*)} \leq \log \frac{1}{P(\beta_j/\alpha_i)} \qquad \text{for all } i \tag{6-52b}$$

Let $P_0(\beta_j)$ represent the probability distribution over the set of output sequences which results if the input sequences α_i are selected according to the probability law which achieves capacity. [The inputs, of course, are *not* selected according to this law; that is why we have used the subscript to differentiate $P_0(\beta_j)$ from $P(\beta_j)$, the actual distribution over the β_j.] We may add $\log P_0(\beta_j)$ to both sides of (6-52b).

$$\log \frac{P_0(\beta_j)}{P(\beta_j/\alpha^*)} \leq \log \frac{P_0(\beta_j)}{P(\beta_j/\alpha_i)} \qquad \text{for all } i \tag{6-53}$$

The quantity

$$\log \frac{P_0(\beta_j)}{P(\beta_j/\alpha_i)}$$

will play a role analogous to that played by hamming distance in our proof for the BSC. For a fixed transmitted sequence α_0, the average value of this new type of "distance" between α_0 and the received sequence is

$$\sum_{B^n} P(\beta_j/\alpha_0) \log \frac{P_0(\beta_j)}{P(\beta_j/\alpha_0)} \tag{6-54}$$

The reason for inserting $P_0(\beta_j)$ in (6-53) is now clear. The summation of (6-54) is -1 times the conditional mutual information $I(\alpha_0; B^n)$ that was defined in Section 5-13. Since $P_0(\beta_j)$ are the probabilities of β_j which result when $I(A^n; B^n) = nC$, the channel capacity of the nth extension, $I(\alpha_0; B^n)$, is independent of α_0, and we have

$$\sum_{B^n} P(\beta_j/\alpha_0) \log \frac{P_0(\beta_j)}{P(\beta_j/\alpha_0)} = -nC \qquad \text{for all } \alpha_0 \tag{6-55}$$

When we receive a symbol β_j out of our channel, therefore, our natural inclination is to hunt for the transmitted code symbol among those (if any) code symbols satisfying

$$\log \frac{P_0(\beta_i)}{P(\beta_j/\alpha_i)} \approx -nC \tag{6-56}$$

In geometrical terms we can say that we draw a sphere† about the received sequence β_j. The sphere includes all code words α_i satisfying

$$\log \frac{P_0(\beta_j)}{P(\beta_j/\alpha_i)} \leq -nC \tag{6-57}$$

We might then hunt for the transmitted sequence α_0 inside this sphere. As before, we add the insurance of ϵ and enlarge the sphere (Figure 6-17) to include those code words satisfying

$$\log \frac{P_0(\beta_j)}{P(\beta_j/\alpha_i)} \leq -nC + n\epsilon = -n(C - \epsilon) \tag{6-58}$$

Our decision procedure will be to draw the sphere defined by (6-58) and, if there is a *unique* code point inside this sphere, we shall decide that such a point was the one transmitted. If there is no unique code point inside the sphere (either because there are

---

† The word *sphere* is used only to suggest the argument used in the case of the BSC. The *radius* of the "sphere" is negative.

none or because there are more than one), we just throw up our hands and make an error!   This procedure will lead to a negligible probability of error.

Using the procedure just described, there are two ways that an error in decoding a received sequence may occur.   Let $S(\epsilon)$ indicate the set of code points satisfying (6-58) (i.e., the set of points in the

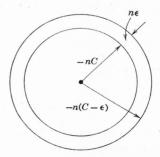

FIGURE 6-17. A sphere including all code points satisfying Equations (6-57) and (6-58).

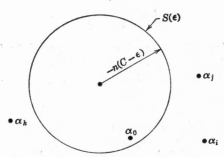

FIGURE 6-18. Correct decoding of β_j.

larger sphere of Figure 6-17).   The first way is if α_0, the transmitted code word, is not in $S(\epsilon)$; the only other way an error can occur is if α_0 is in $S(\epsilon)$ but some other code word is also in $S(\epsilon)$ (Figure 6-18).   Hence, we may write the probability of error as

$$P_E = \mathrm{Pr}\ \{\alpha_0 \not\in S(\epsilon)\} + \mathrm{Pr}\ \{\alpha_0 \in S(\epsilon)\}$$
$$\times \mathrm{Pr}\ \{\text{at least one other code word} \in S(\epsilon)\} \quad (6\text{-}59)$$

where $\in$ and $\not\in$ are read "is contained in" and "is not contained in," respectively.   Using arguments identical with those used to produce (6-38), (6-39), and (6-40), we obtain

$$P_E \le \Pr\{\alpha_0 \not\subseteq S(\epsilon)\} + \Pr\{\text{at least one other code word} \in S(\epsilon)\}$$
(6-60)

$$\Pr\{\text{at least one other code word} \in S(\epsilon)\} \le \sum_{\alpha_i \ne \alpha_0} \Pr\{\alpha_i \in S(\epsilon)\}$$
(6-61)

$$P_E \le \Pr\{\alpha_0 \not\subseteq S(\epsilon)\} + \sum_{\alpha_i \ne \alpha_0} \Pr\{\alpha_i \in S(\epsilon)\}$$
(6-62)

Equation (6-62) expresses a simple bound on the probability of error for a specific set of M code words. The first term of (6-62) is the probability that the transmitted code word α_0 will not satisfy (6-58); the second term is the sum of probabilities (one for each code word not transmitted) that a code word not transmitted will satisfy (6-58).

As before, the first term is bounded by using the law of large numbers; we then apply Shannon's random coding argument to evaluate the second term. As we have seen, the average value of

$$\log \frac{P_0(\beta_j)}{P(\beta_j/\alpha_0)}$$

is $-nC$. This logarithm may be decomposed into the sum of n terms, each involving only one of the n symbols comprising β_j, and one of the n symbols comprising α_0. Hence, by the law of large numbers, if we take n large enough, the probability that the sum will exceed $-nC$ by more than $n\epsilon$ can be made less than δ, where δ is as small as we wish. Equation (6-62) becomes

$$P_E \le \delta + \sum_{\alpha_i \ne \alpha_0} \Pr\{\alpha_i \in S(\epsilon)\}$$
(6-63)

Now we apply the random coding argument. Let $P_0(\alpha_i)$ be the input probabilities which achieve capacity. We select M code words according to these probabilities (again accepting the possibility of a singular code). This time, the r^{Mn} possible codes are not necessarily equiprobable—the probability of selecting any fixed set of M code words is given by the product of the corresponding M probabilities.

We next average (6-63) over the r^{Mn} possible codes to obtain a bound on the average error probability $\widetilde{P_E}$. Using a wavy bar to represent an average over the r^{Mn} codes, we obtain

$$\widetilde{P_E} \leq \delta + \overbrace{\sum_{\alpha_i \neq \alpha_0} \Pr\{\alpha_i \in S(\epsilon)\}}$$
$$\leq \delta + (M - 1) \overline{\Pr\{\alpha_i \in S(\epsilon)\}}$$
$$\leq \delta + M \overline{\Pr\{\alpha_i \in S(\epsilon)\}} \tag{6-64}$$

Up to this point, the steps in our proof have paralleled those in the proof of Shannon's second theorem for the BSC. In order to evaluate $\overline{\Pr\{\alpha_i \in S(\epsilon)\}}$, however, a different argument is necessary. $\overline{\Pr\{\alpha_i \in S(\epsilon)\}}$ is the average of the probability that α_i is contained in $S(\epsilon)$. For a *fixed* β_j, this quantity may be written as $\sum_{S(\epsilon)} P_0(\alpha_i)$. $S(\epsilon)$ depends upon β_j, however, so that the expression we seek is given by [letting $P_0(\beta_j)$ represent the output probabilities resulting when $P_0(\alpha_i)$ are used]

$$\overline{\Pr\{\alpha_i \in S(\epsilon)\}} = \sum_{B^n} P_0(\beta_j) \sum_{S(\epsilon)} P_0(\alpha_i)$$
$$= \sum_{B^n, S(\epsilon)} P_0(\beta_j) P_0(a_i) \tag{6-65}$$

The summation on the right of (6-65) is over all pairs α_i, β_j, such that

$$\log \frac{P_0(\beta_j)}{P(\beta_j/\alpha_i)} \leq -n(C - \epsilon) \tag{6-66}$$

For any such pair,

$$P_0(\beta_j) P_0(\alpha_i) \leq P(\beta_j/\alpha_i) P_0(\alpha_i) 2^{-n(C-\epsilon)} \tag{6-67}$$

Now we sum (6-67) over all pairs satisfying (6-66),

$$\sum_{B^n, S(\epsilon)} P_0(\beta_j) P_0(\alpha_i) \leq 2^{-n(C-\epsilon)} \sum_{B^n, S(\epsilon)} P(\beta_j/\alpha_i) P_0(\alpha_i)$$
$$\leq 2^{-n(C-\epsilon)} \tag{6-68}$$

Equations (6-68) and (6-65) may be used in (6-64) to obtain

$$\boxed{\widetilde{P_E} \leq \delta + M 2^{-n(C-\epsilon)}} \tag{6-69}$$

Equation (6-69) contains the essence of Shannon's second theorem. The parameter δ can be made as small as we wish by increasing the block length n. Hence, the total right side of (6-69) can be made as small as we want, as long as

$$M \leq 2^{n(C-\epsilon')} < 2^{n(C-\epsilon)} \qquad (6\text{-}70)$$

for any $\epsilon' < \epsilon < 0$. This is the expression we seek. We may choose ϵ, and hence ϵ', to be arbitrarily small positive numbers. Then, if M satisfies (6-70), the average probability of error $\widetilde{\widetilde{P}}_E$ can be made less than any preassigned value. There must be at least one code which does as well as the average; so we are assured that there exists a code with almost 2^{nC} code words with error probability arbitrarily small. Therefore, we may send up to

$$\frac{\log 2^{nC}}{n} = C \qquad (6\text{-}71)$$

essentially error-free binary messages with each symbol of a channel of capacity C.

In order to prove the converse to Shannon's second theorem, we employ the Fano inequality (6-23). We wish to show that the probability of error cannot be made arbitrarily small by increasing n if we use $M = 2^{n(C+\epsilon)}$ code words to represent m equiprobable messages. Assume that we use $M = 2^{n(C+\epsilon)}$ code words, each with probability $1/M$. Then, since

$$H(A^n) - H(A^n/B^n) \leq nC \qquad (6\text{-}72)$$

we have

$$\log 2^{n(C+\epsilon)} - H(A^n/B^n) \leq nC$$

or
$$n\epsilon \leq H(A^n/B^n) \qquad (6\text{-}73)$$

But, by the Fano inequality,

$$H(A^n/B^n) \leq H(P_E) + P_E \log M$$
$$\leq 1 + P_E(nC + n\epsilon) \qquad (6\text{-}74)$$

Upon using (6-74) in (6-73), we find

$$P_E \geq \frac{n\epsilon - 1}{nC + n\epsilon} \qquad (6\text{-}75)$$

As n increases, the error probability for any code is bounded away from 0. Hence, we cannot transmit essentially error-free messages at a rate exceeding the channel capacity.

6-11. Epilogue

In the previous section we showed that if we selected code words of length n at random for transmission through a channel of capacity C, the probability of message error would remain small as long as we chose less than 2^{nC} code words. A natural question for communications engineers, therefore, is: "How does one design a code achieving the reliability promised by Shannon's second theorem?"

Of course, one could go to a table of random numbers and use this table to select the code words. Choosing a code at random, however, is not a very satisfying way to design a communication system. Equipment necessary to implement such a system is likely to be impractical. In addition, there is always that annoying possibility (albeit small) that the code selected will not produce a small error probability. Shannon's second theorem has shown that almost all codes have small error probability (after all, we proved the theorem by picking a code at random!). Can we not then find a deterministic method of producing good codes?

This is the dilemma which has persisted to mock information theorists since Shannon's original paper in 1948. Despite an enormous amount of effort (Peterson, 1961) spent since that time in quest of this Holy Grail of information theory, a *deterministic* method of generating the codes promised by Shannon is still to be found.

NOTES

Note 1. In view of the correspondence of information channels to statistical experiments pointed out in Note 1 at the end of Chapter 5, Shannon's second theorem may be viewed as a result dealing with the asymptotic properties of statistical experiments (Abramson, 1960).

Note 2. As mentioned in Section 6-9, the statistical literature contains a number of results showing that for message rates less than capacity the error probability goes to zero exponentially (or sometimes almost exponentially) in the block length n. Sorting out the various members of this error-bound population explosion appears to be a demanding and not very rewarding task. Feinstein (1955) was the first to prove an exponential error bound. In addition, Feinstein's bound applied to the maximum error probability and not just the average error probability. Perhaps the simplest exponential bound is due to Blackwell, Breiman, and Thomasian (1959). They use a bounding technique due to Chernoff (1952) on an equation equivalent to our (6-63) to obtain

$$P_E \leq 2 \exp\left[-\frac{(C-R)^2}{16rs}\, n \right] \quad \text{for } 0 \leq C - R \leq \tfrac{1}{2}$$

where C is the channel capacity, R is the message rate, r is the number of input symbols, s is the number of output symbols, and n is the block length.

Note 3. The channel capacity provides an upper bound to the set of message rates at which we can send information with probability of error arbitrarily *close* to zero. Under certain circumstances, it is possible to transmit messages with the probability of error *equal* to zero. Shannon (1956) defines the *zero error capacity* of an information channel as the least upper bound of message rates at which it is possible to transmit information with zero error probability. For example, consider the channel

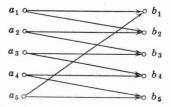

where the probabilities associated with each of the arrows in the above diagram are arbitrary, as long as they satisfy $0 < P_{ij} < 1$. Then, since we may transmit the two input symbols a_1, a_3 with zero probability of error, the zero error capacity is at least 1 bit. This bound may be improved, however, by employing the second extension of this channel. In this case, we may transmit a_1a_1, a_2a_3, a_3a_5, a_4a_2, and a_5a_4 with zero probability of error, so that the zero error capacity is at least $\tfrac{1}{2} \log 5$ bits.

PROBLEMS

6-1. A uniform channel has r inputs. These inputs are chosen with equal probabilities, and it is found that the maximum-likelihood decision procedure produces a probability of error p. Find a *lower* bound to the equivocation $H(A/B)$ in terms of r or p, or both. The lower bound of 0 is not acceptable.

6-2. Find all three maximum-likelihood decision rules for the channel of (6-2).

APPENDIX: TABLES

TABLE A-1. LOGARITHMS TO THE BASE 2

n	$\log n$	n	$\log n$
1	0.000000	26	4.700439
2	1.000000	27	4.754887
3	1.584962	28	4.807355
4	2.000000	29	4.857981
5	2.321928	30	4.906890
6	2.584962	31	4.954196
7	2.807355	32	5.000000
8	3.000000	33	5.044394
9	3.169925	34	5.087463
10	3.321928	35	5.129283
11	3.459431	36	5.169925
12	3.584962	37	5.209453
13	3.700440	38	5.247927
14	3.807355	39	5.285402
15	3.906890	40	5.321928
16	4.000000	41	5.357552
17	4.087463	42	5.392317
18	4.169925	43	5.426264
19	4.247927	44	5.459431
20	4.321928	45	5.491853
21	4.392317	46	5.523562
22	4.459431	47	5.554589
23	4.523562	48	5.584962
24	4.584962	49	5.614710
25	4.643856	50	5.643856

TABLE A-1. LOGARITHMS TO THE BASE 2 (*Continued*)

n	log n	n	log n
51	5.672425	76	6.247927
52	5.700439	77	6.266786
53	5.727920	78	6.285402
54	5.754887	79	6.303780
55	5.781359	80	6.321928
56	5.807355	81	6.339850
57	5.832890	82	6.357552
58	5.857981	83	6.375039
59	5.882643	84	6.392317
60	5.906890	85	6.409391
61	5.930737	86	6.426264
62	5.954196	87	6.442943
63	5.977280	88	6.459431
64	6.000000	89	6.475733
65	6.022367	90	6.491853
66	6.044394	91	6.507794
67	6.066089	92	6.523562
68	6.087462	93	6.539158
69	6.108524	94	6.554588
70	6.129283	95	6.569855
71	6.149747	96	6.584962
72	6.169925	97	6.599912
73	6.189824	98	6.614709
74	6.209453	99	6.629356
75	6.228818	100	6.643856

TABLE A-2. THE ENTROPY FUNCTION $H(p)$
$$H(p) = -p \log p - \bar{p} \log \bar{p}$$

p	$H(p)$	p	$H(p)$
0.005	0.045415	0.130	0.557438
0.010	0.080793	0.135	0.570993
0.015	0.112364	0.140	0.584239
0.020	0.141441	0.145	0.597185
0.025	0.168661	0.150	0.609840
0.030	0.194392	0.155	0.622213
0.035	0.218878	0.160	0.634310
0.040	0.242292	0.165	0.646138
0.045	0.264765	0.170	0.657705
0.050	0.286397	0.175	0.669016
0.055	0.307268	0.180	0.680077
0.060	0.327445	0.185	0.690894
0.065	0.346981	0.190	0.701471
0.070	0.365924	0.195	0.711815
0.075	0.384312	0.200	0.721928
0.080	0.402179	0.205	0.731816
0.085	0.419556	0.210	0.741483
0.090	0.436470	0.215	0.750932
0.095	0.452943	0.220	0.760167
0.100	0.468996	0.225	0.769193
0.105	0.484648	0.230	0.778011
0.110	0.499916	0.235	0.786626
0.115	0.514816	0.240	0.795040
0.120	0.529361	0.245	0.803257
0.125	0.543564	0.250	0.811278

TABLE A-2. THE ENTROPY FUNCTION $H(p)$ (Continued)

$$H(p) = -p \log p - \bar{p} \log \bar{p}$$

p	$H(p)$	p	$H(p)$
0.255	0.819107	0.380	0.958042
0.260	0.826746	0.385	0.961497
0.265	0.834198	0.390	0.964800
0.270	0.841465	0.395	0.967951
0.275	0.848548	0.400	0.970951
0.280	0.855451	0.405	0.973800
0.285	0.862175	0.410	0.976550
0.290	0.868721	0.415	0.979051
0.295	0.875093	0.420	0.981454
0.300	0.881291	0.425	0.983708
0.305	0.887317	0.430	0.985815
0.310	0.893173	0.435	0.987775
0.315	0.898861	0.440	0.989588
0.320	0.904381	0.445	0.991254
0.325	0.909736	0.450	0.992774
0.330	0.914925	0.455	0.994149
0.335	0.919953	0.460	0.995378
0.340	0.924819	0.465	0.996462
0.345	0.929523	0.470	0.997402
0.350	0.934068	0.475	0.998196
0.355	0.938454	0.480	0.998846
0.360	0.942683	0.485	0.999351
0.365	0.946755	0.490	0.999711
0.370	0.950672	0.495	0.999928
0.375	0.954434	0.500	1.000000

REFERENCES

Abramson, N. (1960): A Partial Ordering for Binary Channels, *IRE Trans. Inform. Theory*, vol. 6, no. 5, pp. 529–539, December.

Bar-Hillel, Y., and R. Carnap (1952): Semantic Information, in Willis Jackson (ed.), "Communication Theory," Academic Press Inc., New York.

Basharin, G. P. (1959): On a Statistical Estimate for the Entropy of a Sequence of Independent Random Variables, *Theory Probability Appl.*, vol. 4, no. 3, pp. 333–336.

Bell, D. A. (1953): "Information Theory and Its Engineering Applications," Sir Isaac Pitman & Sons, Ltd., London.

Bellman, R. (1960): "Introduction to Matrix Analysis," McGraw-Hill Book Company, Inc., New York.

Bharucha-Reid, A. T. (1960): "Elements of the Theory of Markov Processes and Their Applications," McGraw-Hill Book Company, Inc., New York.
191

Billingsley, P. (1961): On the Coding Theorem for the Noiseless Channel, *Ann. Math. Statist.*, vol. 32, no. 2, pp. 576–601.

Birnbaum, A. (1961): On the Foundations of Statistical Inference: Binary Experiments, *Ann. Math. Statist.*, vol. 32, no. 2, pp. 414–435, June.

Blachman, N. M. (1961): A Generalization of Mutual Information, *Proc. IRE*, vol. 49, no. 8, pp. 1331–1332, August.

Blackwell, D. (1953): Equivalent Comparisons of Experiments, *Ann. Math. Statist.*, vol. 24, pp. 265–272, June.

———, L. Breiman, and A. J. Thomasian (1958): Proof of Shannon's Transmission Theorem for Finite-state Indecomposable Channels, *Ann. Math. Statist.*, vol. 29, no. 4, pp. 1209–1220, December.

———, ———, and ——— (1959): The Capacity of a Class of Channels, *Ann. Math. Statist.*, vol. 30, pp. 1229–1241, December.

———, ———, and ——— (1960): The Capacities of Certain Channel Classes under Random Coding, *Ann. Math. Statist.*, vol. 31, pp. 558–567, September.

Blyth, C. R. (1958): Note on Estimating Information, *Tech. Rept.* 17, Department of Statistics, Stanford University.

Breiman, L. (1957): The Individual Ergodic Theorem of Information Theory, *Ann. Math. Statist.*, vol. 28, no. 3, pp. 809–811; a correction to this paper is published in *Ann. Math. Statist.*, vol. 31, no. 3, pp. 809–810.

Brillouin, L. (1956): "Science and Information Theory," Academic Press Inc., New York.

Chernoff, H. (1952): A Measure of Asymptotic Efficiency for Tests of a Hypothesis Based on the Sum of Observations, *Ann. Math. Statist.*, vol. 23, pp. 493–507.

Cherry, C. (1957): "On Human Communication," John Wiley & Sons, Inc., New York.

Csiszar, I. (1961): Some Remarks on the Dimension and Entropy of Random Variables, *Acta Math. Acad. Sci. Hung.*, vol. 12, pp. 399–408.

Elias, P. (1953): Optics and Communication Theory, *J. Opt. Soc. Am.*, vol. 43, pp. 229–232, April.

——— (1958): Two Famous Papers, *IRE Trans. Inform. Theory*, vol. 4, no. 3, p. 99, September.

Fano, R. (1949): The Transmission of Information, I, *MIT Res. Lab. Electron. Tech. Rept.* 65.

——— (1950): The Transmission of Information, II, *MIT Res. Lab. Electron. Tech. Rept.* 149.

——— (1961): "Transmission of Information," John Wiley & Sons, Inc., New York.

Feinstein, A. (1955): Error Bounds in Noisy Channels without Memory, *IRE Trans. Inform. Theory*, vol. IT-1, no. 2, pp. 13–14, September.

——— (1958): "Foundations of Information Theory," McGraw-Hill Book Company, Inc., New York.

Feller, W. (1950): "Probability Theory and Its Applications," John Wiley & Sons, Inc., New York.

Gel'fand, I. M., and A. M. Yaglom (1957): Computation of the Amount of Information about a Stochastic Function Contained in Another Such Function, *Usp. Mat. Nauk*, vol. 12, no. 1, pp. 3–52 (in Russian; a translation appears in *Am. Math. Soc. Transl.*, ser. 2, vol. 12, pp. 199–246).

Golomb, S. (1961a): A New Derivation of the Entropy Expressions, *IRE Trans. Inform. Theory*, vol. IT-7, no. 3, pp. 166–167, July.

——— (1961b): Efficient Coding for the Desoxyribonucleic Channel, *Proc. Symp. Appl. Math.*, vol. 14, *Mathematical Problems in the Biological Sciences*, American Mathematical Society, pp. 87–100.

——— (1962): Genetic Coding, *Eng. Sci. Mag.*, California Institute of Technology, April.

Grettenberg, T. L. (1962): The Ordering of Finite Experiments, *Trans. Third Prague Conf. Inform. Theory Statist. Decision Functions*, Publishing House of the Czechoslovak Academy of Sciences, Prague.

Hamming, R. W. (1950): Error Detecting and Error Correcting Codes, *Bell System Tech. J.*, vol. 29, pp. 147–150.

Harman, W. W. (1963): "Principles of the Statistical Theory of Communication," McGraw-Hill Book Company, Inc., New York.

Hartley, R. V. L. (1928): Transmission of Information, *Bell System Tech. J.*, vol. 7, pp. 535–563.

Huffman, D. A. (1952): A Method for the Construction of Minimum Redundancy Codes, *Proc. IRE*, vol. 40, no. 10, pp. 1098–1101, September.

Jaynes, E. T. (1959): A Note on Unique Decipherability, *IRE Trans. Inform. Theory*, vol. 5, pp. 98–102, September.

Karp, R. M. (1961): Minimum-redundancy Coding for the Discrete Noiseless Channel, *IRE Trans. Inform. Theory*, vol. IT-7, pp. 27–38, January.

Karush, J. (1961): A Simple Proof of an Inequality of McMillan, *IRE Trans. Inform. Theory*, vol. IT-7, no. 2, p. 118, April.

Kelly, D. H. (1962): Information Capacity of a Single Retinal Channel, *IRE Trans. Inform. Theory*, vol. IT-8, no. 3, pp. 221–226, April.

Kelly, J. L., Jr. (1956): A New Interpretation of Information Rate, *Bell System Tech. J.*, vol. 35, pp. 917–927.

Kempthorne, O. (1952): "The Design and Analysis of Experiments," John Wiley & Sons, Inc., New York.

Khinchin, A. I. (1957): "Mathematical Foundations of Information Theory," Dover Publications, Inc., New York.

Kraft, L. G. (1949): "A Device for Quantizing, Grouping, and Coding Amplitude Modulated Pulses," M.S. thesis, Electrical Engineering Department, Massachusetts Institute of Technology, March.

Kullback, S. (1959): "Information Theory and Statistics," John Wiley & Sons, Inc., New York.

Lindley, D. (1956): On a Measure of the Information Provided by an Experiment, *Ann. Math. Statist.*, vol. 27, pp. 986–1005.

McGill, W. J. (1954): Multivariate Information Transmission, *IRE Trans. Inform. Theory*, vol. 4, pp. 93–111, September.

McMillan, B. (1953): The Basic Theorems of Information Theory, *Ann. Math. Statist.*, vol. 24, pp. 196–219.

INFORMATION THEORY AND CODING

McMillan, B. (1956): Two Inequalities Implied by Unique Decipherability, *IRE Trans. Inform. Theory*, vol. IT-2, pp. 115–116, December.
Miller, G. A., and W. G. Madow (1954): On the Maximum Likelihood Estimate of the Shannon-Wiener Measure of Information, *Air Force Cambridge Res. Center Rept.*, Cambridge, Mass.
Muroga, S. (1953): On the Capacity of a Discrete Channel I, *J. Phys. Soc. Japan*, vol. 8, pp. 484–494.
——— (1956): On the Capacity of a Discrete Channel, II, *J. Phys. Soc. Japan*, vol. 11, pp. 1109–1120.
Murphy, R. (1962): Adaptive Processes in Economic Systems, *Stanford Univ. Appl. Math. Statist. Lab. Tech. Rept.* 119, July.
Parzen, E. (1960): "Modern Probability Theory and Its Applications," John Wiley & Sons, Inc., New York.
——— (1961): "Stochastic Processes," Holden-Day, Inc., San Francisco.
Perez, A. (1959): Information Theory with an Abstract Alphabet, *Theory Probability Appl.*, vol. 4, no. 1, pp. 99–102.
Peterson, W. W. (1961): "Error-correcting Codes," John Wiley & Sons, Inc., New York.
Pierce, J. R. (1961): "Symbols, Signals and Noise," Harper & Row, Publishers, Incorporated, New York.
——— and J. E. Karlin (1957): Reading Rates and the Information Rate of a Human Channel, *Bell System Tech. J.*, vol. 36, pp. 497–516.
Pinkerton, R. C. (1956): Information Theory and Melody, *Sci. Am.*, pp. 77–87, February.
Pinsker, M. S. (1954): The Quantity of Information about a Gaussian Random Stationary Process, Contained in a Second Process Connected with It in a Stationary Manner, *Dokl. Akad. Nauk SSSR*, pp. 213–216 (in Russian).
Powers, K. H. (1956): A Unified Theory of Information, *MIT Res. Lab. Electron. Tech. Rept.* 311, February.
Pratt, F. (1942): "Secret and Urgent," Doubleday & Company, Inc., Garden City, N.Y.
Quastler, H. (1956): "Information Theory in Psychology," The Free Press of Glencoe, New York.
Renyi, A. (1959): On the Dimension and Entropy of Probability Distributions, *Acta Math. Acad. Sci. Hung.*, vol. 10, pp. 193–215.
Reza, F. M. (1961): "An Introduction to Information Theory," McGraw-Hill Book Company, Inc., New York.
Sardinas, A. A., and G. W. Patterson (1953): A Necessary and Sufficient Condition for the Unique Decomposition of Coded Messages, 1953 *IRE Conv. Record*, pt. 8, pp. 104–108.
Shannon, C. E. (1951): Prediction and Entropy of Printed English, *Bell System Tech. J.*, vol. 30, no. 1, pp. 50–64, January.
——— (1956): The Zero Error Capacity of a Noisy Channel, *IRE Trans. Inform. Theory*, vol. IT-2, no. 3, pp. 8–16, September.
——— (1957a): Certain Results in Coding Theory for Noisy Channels, *Inform. Control*, vol. 1, no. 1, pp. 6–25, September.

———— (1957b): Geometric Interpretation of Some Results of Channel Capacity Calculations, *Nachrichtentechnik*, vol. 10, pp. 1–4.

———— (1958): A Note on a Partial Ordering for Communication Channels, *Inform. Control*, vol. 1, pp. 390–397, December.

———— and W. Weaver (1949): "The Mathematical Theory of Communication," The University of Illinois Press, Urbana, Ill. (The first part of this book is a reprint of Shannon's paper A Mathematical Theory of Communication, *Bell System Tech. J.*, vol. 27, pp. 379–423, 623–656, 1948.)

Silverman, R. A. (1955): On Binary Channels and Their Cascades, *IRE Trans. Inform. Theory*, vol. IT-1, pp. 19–27, December.

Stumpers, F. L. H. M. (1953): A Bibliography of Information Theory, *IRE Trans. Inform. Theory*, vol. PGIT-2, November.

———— (1955): A Bibliography of Information Theory, First Supplement, *IRE Trans. Inform. Theory*, vol. IT-1, pp. 31–47, September.

———— (1957): A Bibliography of Information Theory, Second Supplement, *IRE Trans. Inform. Theory*, vol. IT-3, pp. 150–166, June.

———— (1960): A Bibliography of Information Theory, Third Supplement, *IRE Trans. Inform. Theory*, vol. IT-6, pp. 25–51, March.

Thomasian, A. J. (1960): An Elementary Proof of the AEP of Information Theory, *Ann. Math. Statist.*, vol. 31, pp. 452–456.

Wolfowitz, J. (1959): Strong Converse of the Coding Theorem for Semi-continuous Channels, *Illinois J. Math.*, vol. 3, no. 4, pp. 477–489.

Woodward, P. M. (1955): "Probability and Information Theory, with Applications to Radar," Pergamon Press, New York.

Wozencraft, J. M., and B. Reiffen (1961): "Sequential Decoding," John Wiley & Sons, Inc., New York.

Yaglom, A. M., and I. M. Yaglom (1959): "Probabilité et Information," Dunod, Paris (in French, translated from the Russian).

INDEX